# Law and Management in Optometric Practice

GW00393214

# Law and Management in Optometric Practice

**Steve Taylor** BSc (Hons), MSc, PhD, FBCO, FAAO
Lecturer, Department of Optometry, University of Wales Institute of Science and Technology, Cardiff

and

**David P. Austen** BSc (Hons), MSc, FBCO, FAAO
Independent Optometrist, Loughborough

Butterworths
London  Boston  Durban  Singapore  Sydney  Toronto  Wellington

First published 1986

© Butterworth & Co (Publishers) Ltd, 1986

---

**British Library Cataloguing in Publication Data**

Taylor, Steve
    Law and management in optometric practice.
    1. Opticianry—Law and legislation—Great Britain
    I. Title    II. Austen, David P.
    344.104'41      KD3213.06

    ISBN 0-407-00318-5

---

Photoset by Butterworths Litho Preparation Department
Printed in England by Whitstable Litho Ltd., Whitstable, Kent

# Preface and acknowledgements

In the course of teaching professional law and practice management it became apparent that there was a need for a subject text with which to complement lecture notes. The original statutes and statutory instruments do provide a source of information, but generally the documents are long-winded and considered unintelligible by the average student. One of us (ST) developed a handbook to fill the gap, and it is that which has been extended to produce the law section of the present book.

The management section discusses the various aspects of practice management, distilled by the other author (DPA) from many years as a practitioner and lecturer on the topic.

The aim of the book, therefore, is to provide a useful text for undergraduate and pre-registration students and to offer a source of very rapid reference for practitioners with queries on law or with management problems.

The details included are correct at the time of going to press but obviously the subject matter is dynamic. Nevertheless, after the recent rapid changes experienced in the ophthalmic profession it is time to take stock.

A number of organisations have been kind enough to allow the use of previously published data, and I am grateful to the British College of Ophthalmic Opticians (Optometrists), Her Majesty's Stationery Office, the New Zealand Optometrical Association, *The Optician* journal and the Royal Society for the Prevention of Accidents for permission to reproduce material, and to Don Schaeffer, secretary of the International Optometric and Optical League, for information on optometry in the EEC. We thank Sue Deeley and Gillian Clarke of Butterworths for their constant attention and help with the manuscript, and our wives and families for their help and understanding during the production of the manuscript.

Steve Taylor
David P. Austen

# Introduction*

The eyes and the law have been intimately connected since the time of Hamurabi. Probably the most quoted and best known legal phrase is a translation of Hamurabi's original code of ethics 'an eye for an eye and a tooth for a tooth'. As Hamurabi is taken as the father of the legal system, then the eyes were even in those days considered important enough to be included at the birth.

The importance of the eye in society has maintained its high status. The early practitioners of ocular health ran a very great risk of loss of limb and financial ruin. In the Greek codes of law a practitioner would lose his hands if he were to treat a nobleman and cause the loss of an eye. Should the eye belong to a servant, then the practitioner was expected to replace the servant if the treatment resulted in the loss of an eye. In view of the state of understanding (or lack of it) of surgery and intraocular disorders, and the inability to see into the eye before commencing treatment, it is surprising that anyone ventured into the risky business of ophthalmology. The advent of modern techniques and changes in the legal system have obviously helped to produce a healthier number of optical specialists, all with both hands intact!

The optical profession in Europe as separate from the professions of medicine and ophthalmology can obviously be traced back to the invention of spectacles. It is difficult to put a date on this as the initial years of spectacle production are shrouded in mystery. Marco Polo, reporting on his travels in China in 1275, mentioned that people wore glasses before their eyes for reading. The first evidence of the development of spectacles in Europe dates their invention to about AD 1280. Documents still exist in Venice, however, which refer to the manufacture of a form of spectacles which appeared in the first half of the thirteenth century. This evidence contradicts the general theory that a Florentinian, Salvino Degli Armati, was the inventor. He was credited with the invention in an inscription said to exist in a tomb in the church of Santa Maria Maggiore:

> 'Here lies Salvino Degli Armati son of Armato of Florence inventor of eyeglasses. May God forgive his sins. AD 1317.'

* Taken from Taylor, S. (1982) Optometric law. *Optician,* **184,** no. 4757, 10.

The tomb is no longer in existence, and recent research has cast doubt upon the validity of the inscription.

It would seem that spectacles were definitely in use by 1282, when a reference in the records of the Abbey of Saint Bavon le Grand, indicates that a priest called Nicholas Bullett used spectacles when signing an agreement. It may be, however, that spectacles were re-invented by a Dominican monk who kept the invention secret for commercial reasons. The evidence to support this comes from a reference in the Lenten Sermon on 23 February 1305 in the church of Santa Maria Novella in Florence. The sermon was given by Giordarno da Rivalto, who credited Friar Della Spina with the invention.

As a legal body, spectacle makers in Europe were first introduced into a Guild by Louis XI in France in 1465. At this time the Guild also included haberdashers and upholsterers. This was changed in 1581 when Henry III granted a new guild consisting of mirror makers, toy makers and spectacle makers. The first German Guild of spectacle makers was established in Nuremberg in 1577. The Guild had the function of maintaining law and order within its profession.

In Britain, the spectacle makers were incorporated by Royal Charter granted by Charles I on 16 May 1629. The Charter, giving permission to form the Spectacle Makers Company, provided the opportunity to create laws and to produce a profession. It became a 'closed shop', with the Company granting only certain people, who had trained for their craft, permission to practise their trade. The original Charter gave the Court of the Spectacle Makers the power to make 'laws and statutes, decrees, ordinances and constitutions for the good rule and government of the Fellowship and craft'.

The Spectacle Makers Company began to lose a little control in the late eighteenth century, and the British Optical Association was eventually formed as an organising body in 1895. The function of the BOA was to improve standards within the profession, and an examination system was quickly established. Not to be outdone, the Spectacle Makers introduced their own examinations in 1898. The Spectacle Makers Company examinations at this time were mainly practical and biased towards the manufacturers of lenses and frame materials. Sight testing was not incorporated into the examination syllabus until 1904.

Since these early days of the formation of the nucleus of a profession there has been a rapid rise in the standards of education and a requirement for registration. To meet the changes various legislative orders have been introduced. The advances in the law relating to ocular health directly relevant to the practising optometrist will be outlined in the chapters which follow, together with the principles of sound practice management.

# Contents

# Part II  Management in Optometric Practice

**Part I**

# Law in Optometric Practice

# 1
# The National Health Service

## Establishment of the National Health Service

On 6 November 1946 an Act to establish a comprehensive health service for England and Wales was passed by Parliament. This was the birth of the National Health Service. According to the National Health Service Act 1946, it was the :

'... duty of the Minister of Health ... to promote the establishment in England and Wales of a comprehensive health service designed to secure improvement in the physical and mental health of the people of England and Wales and the prevention, diagnosis and treatment of illness, and for that purpose to provide or secure the effective provision of services in accordance with the following provisions of this Act.'

The National Health Service Act 1946 was set up according to four principles:

1. The health service should be financed by taxes and contributions paid when people were well rather than by charges levied on them when they were sick; and the financial burden of sickness should be spread over the whole community.
2. The health service should be truly national, aiming at providing the same high quality of service in every part of the country.
3. The service should provide full clinical freedom to the doctors working within it.
4. The health service should be centred upon the family doctor team, providing the essential continuity to the health care of each individual and family, and mobilizing the services needed.

Since the National Health Service Act 1946 the following further relevant legislation has been enacted:

National Health Service (Scotland) Act 1947
Health Services Act (Northern Ireland) 1948
National Health Service (Amendment) Act 1949
National Health Service Act 1951
National Health Service Act 1952

National Health Service Act 1961
Health Services and Public Health Act 1968
National Health Service Reorganisation Act 1973
National Health Service Act 1977
Health Services Act 1980
Health and Social Security Act 1984

The gradual changes brought about by these Acts have produced a present-day situation which bears only a slight resemblance to that originally proposed. The changes can be best demonstrated by a rapid resumé of the principal Acts; these are:

National Health Service Act 1946
Health Services and Public Health Act 1968
National Health Service Reorganisation Act 1973

Under the original 1946 enactment the administration of the health service was divided into four main branches:

1. The Minister, as central planner and co-ordinator, would oversee each of the other branches and plan to integrate these as a whole, and would also accept ultimate responsibility for the services.
2. The hospital and specialist services were to be administered on a regional basis by hospital boards, the exception being the teaching hospitals. To ensure maximum efficiency the hospitals were further divided into local groups managed by hospital management committees.
3. Domiciliary care (not treatment) was to be provided by the local authorities and included:
   (a) the care of expectant mothers and young children;
   (b) domiciliary midwifery;
   (c) home nursing and health visiting;
   (d) vaccination and immunisation;
   (e) ambulance services and health centres;
   (f) the care of physically and mentally handicapped.
4. The general practitioner services were to be administered by the executive councils established under Part IV of the National Health Service Act 1946, s. 31. Normally the executive councils were to be responsible for the services in the area of a local health authority, ensuring that there were sufficient practitioners within their area and administering the remuneration and terms and conditions of service.

In order to assist the Minister and to give advice on general matters relating to the administration of the health services a Central Health Services Council was established. In a further effort to maximise efficiency the Minister had the right to constitute standing advisory committees to provide specialist information on any specific aspects of the health services as and when it was required. These advisory committees fell into nine groups:

1. Standing Medical Advisory Committee.
2. Standing Dental Advisory Committee.
3. Standing Pharmaceutical Advisory Committee.
4. Standing Ophthalmic Advisory Committee.
5. Standing Nursing Advisory Committee.

6. Standing Maternity and Midwifery Advisory Committee.
7. Standing Mental Health Advisory Committee.
8. Standing Tuberculosis Advisory Committee.
9. Standing Council and Radiotherapy Advisory Committee.

This, then, provided a sound central administration with the ability to examine carefully any specialist problems which might arise.

In the case of the executive councils, a specialist knowledge was even more readily available. The 25 members of an executive council included: seven members appointed by the local medical committee, three members appointed by the local dental committee and two members appointed by the local pharmaceutical committee.

The local representative committees were formed where the Minister was satisfied that for the areas of any executive council, the committees were representative of: the medical practitioners of the area, the dental practitioners of the area and the people providing pharmaceutical services in the area.

Representatives of the ophthalmic opticians and dispensing opticians providing supplementary ophthalmic services in the area were not formally recognised until the 1949 Act. In spite of the recognition shown by this Act, ophthalmic membership of an executive council was not forthcoming until the Health Services and Public Health Act of 1968.

## Role of the Minister of Health

Under the terms of the National Health Service Act 1946 the Minister was given the ultimate responsibility for the health service and was seen as the co-ordinator. The responsibilities and the position of the Minister could be summarised as follows.

1. Central controller and planner, basing decisions on the information from the Central Council and the standing advisory committees.
2. Maker of detailed rules, regulations and orders (subject to the control of Parliament) by which the health service was to be controlled.
3. Securer of parliamentary sanction for continued financing of the service, with added responsibilities of monitoring costs of the service, approving expenditure and reporting back to Parliament on matters of expenditure.
4. Default and inquiry powers which gave sanction to decisions and requests.
5. To acquire and own, on behalf of the government, land needed for the purposes of the Act.
6. Responsible for all new legislation relating to the health services and many other matters relating to welfare and environmental health.

This vast degree of responsibility made the Minister the integral part of the NHS, without whom the various units could not function to provide a comprehensive and truly national health service.

## The National Health Service Act 1946 relating to optical services

The ophthalmic services to be offered under this legislation were to be known as the supplementary ophthalmic services. The reason for this title was that the original ideal of the health service providing full eye care within the confines of the hospital eye service could not be achieved, and supplementary help was therefore enlisted to meet the demand. In June 1946 the Minister of Health established the Eye Services Committee whose function was to look at and report on:

1. The status, the scope of work and the designation of opticians in the final form of the national ophthalmic services as envisaged in the original National Health Service Act 1946.
2. The criteria to be applied when selecting opticians for appointment in the (temporary) supplementary eye services.

The Committee was formed by representatives of ophthalmologists, medical practitioners and ophthalmic and dispensing opticians. The role of opticians in the proposed National Health Service was established on the basis of the Eye Services Committee report published in May 1947. As a result of the report, the Central Professional Committee for Opticians was established, in November 1947, to consider all applications to work in the supplementary ophthalmic services. Any optician applying to work in the health services was required to give evidence of qualification and of adequate experience.

By the time the health service was operational in July of 1948 it became a duty of the newly formed executive councils to establish services in connection with the diagnosis and treatment of disease or defect of the eyes and the supply of optical appliances. To ensure an adequate specialist service the duties of the executive council in the field of ophthalmics were to be exercised on behalf of the council by a committee called the ophthalmic services committee.

Regulations were made to include provision for:

1. The preparation and publication of lists of medical practitioners, of ophthalmic opticians and of dispensing opticians who undertook to provide supplementary ophthalmic services.
2. Conferring the right of inclusion in the appropriate list on all having an eligible qualification.
3. Conferring on any person the right to choose who should test his or her eyes and who should supply the prescribed appliance.
4. The removal from the list of ophthalmic or dispensing opticians undertaking to provide supplementary ophthalmic services the name of any ophthalmic or dispensing optician who had never provided or who had ceased to provide such services.

The National Health Service Act 1946 also resulted in the establishment of an optical Whitley Committee, the purpose of which was to negotiate salaries for hospital opticians, fees for opticians working part time within the hospital eye service and fees for opticians working in the supplementary ophthalmic services.

Essentially, the original legislation set out to make provisions such that everyone was eligible for free eye examination and free spectacles within the supplementary ophthalmic services. Prior to this a relatively small percentage of people had been eligible for certain optical benefits by way of the additional benefit provisions of the National Health Insurance Acts.

## Health Services and Public Health Act 1968

The Health Services and Public Health Act 1968 was intended:

'to amend the National Health Service Act 1946 and the National Health Service (Scotland) Act 1947 and make other amendments connected with the national health service; to make amendments connected with local authorities' services under the National Assistance Act 1948; to amend the law relating to notifiable diseases and food poisoning; to amend the Nurseries and Child-Minders Regulation Act 1948; to amend the law relating to food and drugs; to enable assistance to be given to certain voluntary organisations; to enable the Minister of Health* and the Secretary of State† to purchase goods for supply to certain authorities; to make other amendments in the law relating to the public health; and for purposes connected with the matters aforesaid.'

As can be seen, this was a wide-ranging piece of legislation.

## Effect of the Health Services and Public Health Act 1968 on optical services

The effect of this legislation on the supplementary ophthalmic services was beneficial. The executive councils had their membership increased from 25 to 30, and for the first time one ophthalmic optician and one dispensing optician acted as representatives nominated from the local optical committee.

This legislation also put the ophthalmic services on a permanent footing; it became known as the general ophthalmic service and not the supplementary ophthalmic service. The old ophthalmic services committee, whose job (on behalf of the executive councils) had been to assess the qualifications of those wishing to offer ophthalmic services in areas where they were needed, could thus be dissolved. (This was included under the terms of the new Health Services and Public Health Act.) In addition, s. 18(3) provided an amendment to the National Health Service Act 1946, allowing for the provision of general ophthalmic services at health centres by ophthalmic medical practitioners, ophthalmic opticians and dispensing opticians.

Finally, ophthalmic and dispensing opticians were defined as follows.

1. 'Ophthalmic optician' means a person listed in either of the registers, maintained under s. 2 of the Opticians Act 1958, of ophthalmic opticians, or bodies corporate enrolled in the list, maintained under s. 4 of the Opticians Act 1958, of such bodies carrying on business as ophthalmic opticians.
2. 'Dispensing optician' means a person listed in the register, maintained under s. 2 of the Opticians Act 1958, of dispensing opticians, or bodies

* Minister of Health. Ministers are chosen by the Prime Minister and appointed by the Crown on the Prime Minister's advice. The Minister of Health is in charge of the Department of Health and responsible for all decisions taken by the Department.
† Secretary of State for Health and Social Security. This is one of the Crown's Principal Secretaries of State, responsible for the administration of the Health and Social Security Department. Constitutionally they act as a channel of communication between the Crown and its subjects.

corporate enrolled in the list, maintained under s. 4 of the 1958 Opticians Act, of such bodies carrying on business as dispensing opticians.

## National Health Service Reorganisation Act 1973

It was decided that, despite the amendments of the 1968 Act and the fact that the NHS had certainly lived up to the four principles upon which it was based, there was a certain need for streamlining. Four objectives had to be met in the reorganisation:

1. The uniting of existing separate services, followed by their integration at local level.
2. The establishment of close links between the unified service and the public health and social services provided by local authorities.
3. The maximum responsibility for administering the service consistent with national plans and priorities should be placed on area health authorities. There should be strong local and professional participation and community involvement in the running of the services in any particular district.
4. The provision for effective central control over money spent on the service and to obtain maximum value.

It was decided that the NHS should be provided and financed by central government. This meant that a boundary had to be drawn between the types of services administered by the health authority and those administered by the local authority.

The National Health Service Reorganisation Act was eventually placed on the statute books in 1973. The new Act still placed the Minister at the head of the services but required also that the following should be provided:

1. Hospital accommodation.
2. Other accommodation for the purposes of any service provided under the National Health Service Acts.
3. Medical, dental, nursing and ambulance services.
4. Such other facilities for the care of expectant and nursing mothers and young children as are considered appropriate as part of the health service.
5. Such facilities for the prevention of illness and for the care of persons suffering from illness as are considered appropriate as part of the health service. (These facilities replaced the arrangements made by the local health authorities under s. 12 of the Health Services and Public Health Act 1968.)
6. Such other services as are required for the diagnosis and treatment of illness.

In addition to the above provisions, there should be arrangements for regular and adequate checks of schoolchildren for both medical and dental health. Also a regular family planning service was established.

The local administration set-up was now directly under the control of the Minister and in the form of:

1. Regional health authorities.
2. Area health authorities.

3. Area health authorities (teaching) if any tuition was undertaken at the hospitals within the area.

In this administrative system the Minister could direct any of the authorities to carry out any function on his behalf related to the National Health Service Acts. The regional health authority could direct an area health authority within its own region to carry out any function relating to the National Health Service Acts, with the proviso that the Minister could counter such directive.

It became the task of the area health authorities to establish family practitioner committees (FPCs) to replace the executive councils and administer the provision of:

1. General medical services.
2. General dental services.
3. General pharmaceutical services.
4. General ophthalmic services.

The FPC comprised:

1. Eleven members appointed by the area health authority.
2. Four members appointed by the local authority (or jointly if two or more local authorities were entitled to appoint members).
3. Eight members appointed by the local medical committee of whom one must be an ophthalmic medical practitioner.
4. Three members appointed by the local dental committee.
5. Two members appointed by the local pharmaceutical committee.
6. One ophthalmic optician appointed by the local optical committee.
7. One dispensing optician appointed by the local optical committee.

In addition to these, formal recognition was given to a committee where the Secretary of State was satisfied that the committee was formed for the region of a regional health authority, as representative of any of the following:

1. Medical practitioners of the region.
2. Dental practitioners of the region.
3. Nurses and midwives of the region.
4. Registered pharmacists of the region.
5. Registered ophthalmic and dispensing opticians of the region.
6. Any group of representatives of other categories providing services.

**Effect of the National Health Service Reorganisation Act 1973 on ophthalmic opticians**

As far as the ophthalmic services were concerned, this legislation had little effect. The local optical committee became a firmly established part of the area health authority and gave the optical profession a voice in the administrative system at local level. The only other change was simply one of name, with the executive council becoming the family practitioner committee without any alteration in the optical representation or duties.

## National Health Service Act 1977

This Act was issued in order:

'to consolidate certain provisions relating to the health service for England and Wales; and to repeal certain enactments relating to the health service which have ceased to have any effect'.

Part I of the Act dealt with services and administration at national and local levels. It set out the duties of the Secretary of State as regards health services. Also under Part I the Secretary of State was required to establish councils termed community health councils, and it was a statutory duty that all parts of area health authorities be included within the district of a community health countil. The composition of these councils was outlined in Sch. 7 of the Act, and the duties were:

1. To represent in the health service the interests of the public in their district.
2. To perform other functions as laid down within the Schedule. These other functions were to include:
   (a) to visit and inspect premises controlled by the relevant area health authority;
   (b) to consider matters relating to the operation of the health service within their district and advise the area health authorities;
   (c) to prepare and publish reports on the operation of the health service within their district.

Part II of the National Health Service Act 1977 dealt specifically with general medical, general dental, general ophthalmic and pharmaceutical services. As far as the general ophthalmic services were concerned, the Act required that every area health authority arrange for medical practitioners with the prescribed qualifications and ophthalmic opticians to provide a service for the testing of sight and for suitably qualified ophthalmic and dispensing opticians to supply optical appliances.

Section 39 required that lists be drawn up of suitably qualified practitioners who would undertake to provide general ophthalmic services. Any person suitably qualified wishing to be included in the appropriate list should be so included. It also made provision for the general public to choose whomsoever they wished to test their eyes and whomsoever they wished to supply the appliance. A final note related to removal of the name of anyone included in the list who had never provided or who had ceased to provide such general ophthalmic services in the area.

Part III of the Act discussed other powers of the Secretary of State relating to the health service. Regulations relating to the changes for dental or optical appliances were laid down in s. 78, which referred to para. 2 of Sch. 12 to this Act. The schedule gave details of the interpretation of the term 'current specified cost' as related to spectacle frames. It also listed details of exemptions from normal costs, including children under 16 years of age or receiving full-time education in school. The information was related to the terms of service for ophthalmic opticians as laid down in SI 1974/287.

Part IV related to property and to finance for the health authorities.

Part V detailed the terms of service of a Health Service Commissioner for England and a Health Service Commissioner for Wales.

Part VI related to miscellaneous items not falling within these other categories.

## Health Service Act 1980

The effect of this legislation was to replace the area health authorities with local district health authorities.

The development of the health service and the role of the ophthalmic services within the overall picture is presented in *Figures 1.1* and *1.2*, showing the interrelationships within the health service as they existed immediately after the introduction of the National Health Service Act 1946 and at the present time.

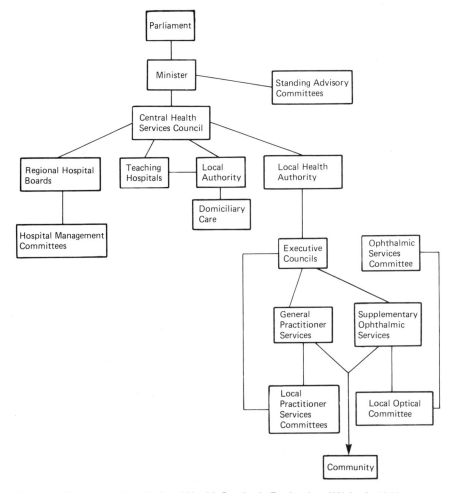

*Figure 1.1* Structure of the National Health Service in England and Wales in 1946

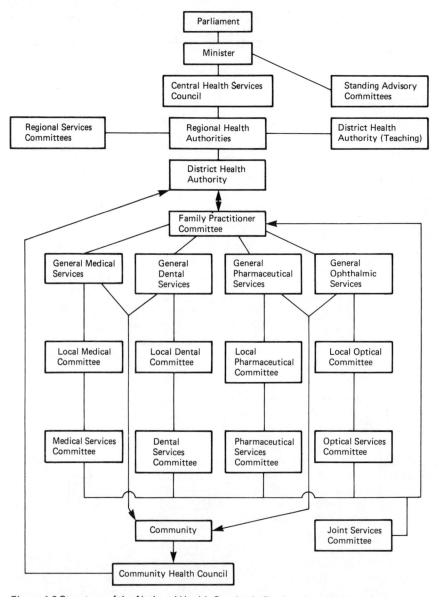

*Figure 1.2* Structure of the National Health Service in England and Wales today

## Regional variations in NHS legislation with respect to ophthalmic services

The foregoing section has dealt with legislation passed by Parliament in London, and although there is little variation in the regions these regulations apply specifically to England and Wales. During the development of the National Health Service there have been, for either environmental or political reasons, separate sets of regulations to cover Scotland and Northern Ireland.

## Scotland

Although separate legislation exists for the NHS in Scotland, for the most part the general ophthalmic services provided are the same as in England and Wales. The most significant differences exist in the administrative structure and in the provision of services for remote areas.

The administration is controlled by the Scottish Home and Health Department which established 15 health boards. The health boards administer hospitals and are responsible for the provision of services which the FPCs provide in England and Wales. This structure is shown in *Figure 1.3*.

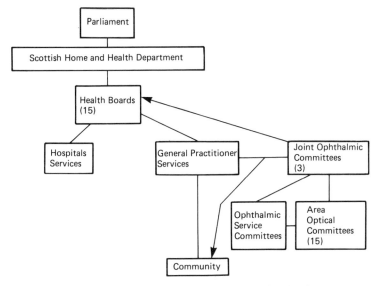

*Figure 1.3* Structure of the National Health Service in Scotland

The general ophthalmic services are arranged on behalf of the health boards by three joint ophthalmic committees. It is the responsibility of these committees to establish the ophthalmic lists. The committees also have power to investigate breaches of NHS contracts either directly or via service committees. Corresponding to the areas of the joint ophthalmic committee there is provision for the recognition of three joint area optical committees. As in England and Wales, practitioner representatives form area optical committees which correspond to the local optical committees of England and Wales. These area optical committees are set up for each of the health board areas.

The second major difference between the service provided is with respect to remote areas where patients may not be able to visit a practitioner without either an excessive journey or an overnight stay. In these areas it is possible for the joint ophthalmic committee to make arrangements, after discussion with the joint area ophthalmic committee for that region and subject to approval by the Secretary of State, to reimburse expenses for an ophthalmic medical practitioner or ophthalmic optician to provide ophthalmic services on a regular basis.

### Northern Ireland

As with Scotland, the major differences between the ophthalmic services of Northern Ireland and those of England and Wales lie in the administrative structure, headed by the Northern Ireland Department of Health and Social Services. The hospitals and practitioner services are administered by four health and social services boards under the authority of that Department. The general ophthalmic services are therefore established by the health and social services boards but they are administered in part by a Central Services Agency, the functions of which are to maintain the ophthalmic lists and to pay fees and reimbursements to ophthalmic medical practitioners, ophthalmic opticians and dispensing opticians. The Agency itself is advised and assisted by the Ophthalmic Committee and an Ophthalmic Officer. This structure is shown in *Figure 1.4.*

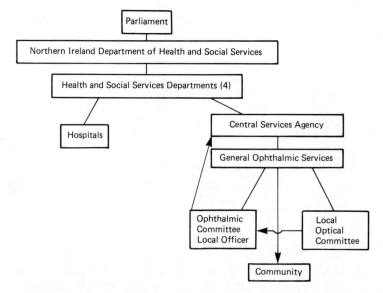

*Figure 1.4* Structure of the National Health Service in Northern Ireland

The other major difference in the ophthalmic services relates to the provision of services to schoolchildren. This section provides for medical practitioners to visit schools, test sight and give a prescription which is to be taken to either an ophthalmic optician or a dispensing optician registered to offer general ophthalmic services.

# 2

# National Health Service (General Ophthalmic Services) Regulations 1974

These regulations (SI* 1974/287) followed in the wake of the National Health Service Reorganisation Act 1973 and contained details of the requirements for working within the general ophthalmic services. The Regulations included details concerning acceptable qualifications, the formation of local lists, the payment of fees and the terms of service for practitioners involved.

### General arrangements for ophthalmic services

The Secretary of State was empowered, after consultation with organisations recognised as representative of contractors (i.e. ophthalmic medical practitioners, ophthalmic opticians/optometrists, dispensing opticians) providing general ophthalmic services, to make provisions regarding:

1. The fees payable by the family practitioner committee (FPC) for the testing of sight by ophthalmic medical practitioners and ophthalmic opticians/ optometrists.
2. The types and the quality of optical appliances which might be supplied under the general ophthalmic services.
3. The payments made by FPCs in respect of the supply, replacement or repair of optical appliances.
4. The type of optical appliance covered by s.44 of the National Health Service Act 1946 (i.e. optical appliances supplied which were of a private type).
5. The current specified costs in relation to frames (this was defined in the schedule to the National Health Service Act 1951).
6. The standard types of children's frames available.
7. The charges to patients for the supply of private spectacle frames as described in item 4, above.
8. The forms designed for use in the provision of general ophthalmic services.

* Statutory instrument (SI). These are rules and regulations made by ministers and government departments under the authority of a statute. Many statutory instruments are required to be laid before Parliament for approval and some are automatically brought into effect by affirmative resolution.

## Ophthalmic lists

The FPCs were required, under SI 1974/287, to prepare lists relating to the provision of general ophthalmic services. The lists were divided into three parts, the first part relating to ophthalmic medical practitioners within the area, the second relating to ophthalmic opticians and the third part relating to dispensing opticians. The lists contained the names of all those persons or bodies corporate within the area who provided services within the scope of the general ophthalmic services. The lists were required to contain the following information.

1. The full names of the persons or bodies corporate entitled to be included.
2. The address of any place within the FPC area at which general ophthalmic services were to be provided.
3. Particulars of the days on which services were usually available at each listed address.
4. The name of each ophthalmic medical practitioner or optician who regularly attended at each listed address to provide services within the general ophthalmic services.

Copies of the lists were circulated to members of the local medical committee and the local optical committee, and any alterations to the list were notified at three-monthly intervals.

## Inclusion in and withdrawal from the ophthalmic lists

The ophthalmic lists are still maintained. Any ophthalmic medical practitioner or qualified optician who wishes to be included in the relevant list and who has the necessary qualifications, is simply required to submit a request for inclusion, containing the details listed above, to the relevant FPC. Once a name is included, however, a contractor is required to notify details of any changes to the entry within 14 days of their occurrence.

Any contractor listed may request that he or she be withdrawn from the list at any time, provided that this is done in writing. On receiving such a request the FPC will remove the name after three months, or less if agreed by that Committee. The FPC will refuse a request to withdraw a name if a tribunal decision relating to fitness to practise is pending or if satisfactory arrangements for the completion of all outstanding services have not been made.

The FPC can remove a contractor's name from the list if they have reason to believe that:

1. The contractor has died.
2. The contractor has for other reasons ceased to be a doctor or qualified optician.
3. The contractor has not provided general ophthalmic services for the preceding six months. (Under this section (s. 9), before making any final decision the FPC must give the contractor 28 days' notice of intention and allow the contractor the opportunity to make representation for retention of his/her name on the list. The exception to this rule is where the contractor is called up to serve in the armed forces; here the six-month period will not begin until after completion of that service.

## Acceptability for sight tests (eye examinations)

Under the terms of the SI 1974/287, patients wishing to have their eyes examined for the first time were required to obtain a form (GOS 1) from their general medical practitioner. This particular condition was repealed under the terms of the National Health Service (General Ophthalmic Services) Amendment Regulations 1977, SI 1977/1999. Any patient can now therefore apply to any ophthalmic medical practitioner or ophthalmic optician whose name appears on the ophthalmic list for an eye examination.

The contractor to whom a person applies for eye examination must, prior to carrying out the examination, secure completion and signing of form GOS 2 by the patient. The form GOS 2 gives full particulars of the patient, and the approximate date of the last eye examination if any. From the details on the form the ophthalmic medical practitioner or ophthalmic optician must satisfy himself/herself that:

1. The patient is entitled to apply for an eye examination.
2. An eye examination appears necessary.

In the event of doubt over either of the above criteria for eligibility for an eye examination, formal application has to be made by the patient to the local FPC. Only with the approval of the FPC can the practitioner then proceed with the eye examination.

## Supply of spectacles

Further regulations are included in SI 1974/287 to cover the supply of an optical appliance following an eye examination. Once issued to the patient the prescription, on form GOS 2B, is valid for presentation to any optician whose name appears in the list of the FPC. This regulation is amended by the Health and Social Security Act 1984 such that the prescription remains valid for two years and, except in certain circumstances as outlined in Chapter 4, may be presented to any person engaged in the supply of spectacles whether or not registered by the FPC.

A patient is also able, under the terms of SI 1974/287, to request that lenses supplied under the general ophthalmic services be fitted to a frame of a more expensive type than prescribed under the GOS (although this situation is likely to be amended following the Health and Social Security Act 1984).

Any lens supplied under the general ophthalmic services was required, prior to April 1985, to meet certain requirements.

1. It had to be of specified shape (i.e. round, pantoscopic round oval, quadra, contour or half eye).
2. The frame had to have a protective rim all the way round. This meant that rimless and nylon Supra frames were not acceptable under the Regulations.
3. The lens could not exceed standard blank size, although the standard size was not specified.
4. The lens had to be of a type acceptable to and listed as available under the general ophthalmic services. This meant that executive and 'D' segment bifocals, for example, were not allowed.

## Replacement and repair of spectacles

A patient may apply to any optician registered with the FPC for replacement or repair of spectacles. Where it appears to an optician that a patient is entitled to a repair under the health service regulations, the relevant form GOS 2R must be completed by or on behalf of the patient. By definition, the replacement of spectacles under the general ophthalmic services means the supply in place of complete or part of spectacles previously supplied under the general ophthalmic services, which have been lost, damaged or destroyed and which are of the same prescription. Repairs covered by the Statement of Fees and Charges are:

1. Solder repairs to metal frames.
2. Replacement of complete or part frames.
3. Replacement of a pair of lenses or one lens.

The only proviso is that the original appliance was supplied under the general ophthalmic services.

Prior to April 1985, adult patients had to pay the whole cost of the repair as specified unless they could prove to the satisfaction of the FPC that the loss or damage was not due to a lack of care. If a complete set of spectacles or a complete new frame was supplied then the patient had to pay the whole cost of the frame whether or not the loss or damage was due to lack of care.

Exceptions to the above were children under the age of 16 and attending full-time education or those below the age of 19 and still attending full-time education. In the case of an applicant under the age of 16, an eye examination was required if the patient had not been seen within the previous 12 months. With the removal of the supply of NHS spectacles to anyone other than groups exempted under the Health and Social Security Act 1984 these regulations are likely to be modified.

## Terms of service

The terms of service for those employed under the general ophthalmic services are laid down in Sch. 1 of SI 1974/287. These Regulations supersede all previous statutory instruments with the exception of rules included in SI 1956/1077, SI 1965/1366 and SI 1969/354 relating to:

1. Investigation and action by the FPC following investigation by the ophthalmic services committee.
2. Appeals to the Secretary of State on decisions under item 1, above.
3. Investigations of overprescribing.

Under the terms of service outlined in Sch. 1 of SI 1974/287, a practitioner is expected to comply with the requirements set out in the various sections.

## *General arrangements*

A contractor is required to make all the necessary arrangements for the provision of services to his patient. This includes registering the practice and keeping the required forms in stock.

## Premises and equipment

The contractor is expected to provide adequate consulting, fitting and waiting room accommodation. There is, however, no specific dimensional requirement for any of these. In addition, there should be suitable equipment for the provision of the general ophthalmic services, although no specific list is given.

In order to ensure adequate standards within the general ophthalmic services, the ophthalmic services committee may make a written request to examine premises. The contractor is required, on receipt of such a request, to admit any such authorised person at all reasonable times.

## Case records

A contractor is required to keep a proper record in respect of each patient seen under the general ophthalmic services. These must be kept for a minimum period of seven years, during which time the contractor may be asked to produce a record for an authorised officer within 14 days of any such request. The record should contain details of the eye examination, the supply of spectacles or the replacement or repair of optical appliances as appropriate.

## Deputies

If a regular arrangement is made for another optician to visit premises to examine eyes or to dispense spectacles then the FPC must be notified of the arrangement and the contractor must ensure that the deputy's name appears on the local list. The contractor is held responsible for the acts or omissions of the deputy while employed. When arranging deputies, an ophthalmic medical practitioner may arrange for eyes to be examined on his behalf only by another ophthalmic medical practitioner; similarly, an ophthalmic optician may arrange for sight to be tested on his behalf only by another ophthalmic optician. An optician may arrange for optical appliances to be supplied, replaced or repaired on his behalf by another optician provided his/her name appears on the list.

## Payments

Any claims for fees are sent to the FPC on the appropriate forms within six months of the completion of the service. All claims must be signed and initialled in ink by the contractor or his deputy. The contractor is not entitled to claim payments from patients for work undertaken under the general ophthalmic services except as laid down in the Statement of Fees. Exceptions to this are payments for fees lost from failure of the patient to keep an appointment and reimbursements of expenses incurred when travelling at the request of the patient to the patient's residence for domiciliary visits.

## Sight testing

Once a contractor has accepted a patient for a sight test, the examination must be carried out with proper care and attention. The examination must be a full and complete examination. If, after the examination, the contractor is of the opinion that the patient needs an optical appliance then the patient must be notified accordingly and given, on the correct form, a copy of the prescription for the supply of that appliance.

The contractor is required to inform that patient's general practitioner if, after examination:

1. It appears that no optical appliance is necessary and the patient is complaining of symptoms.
2. Any abnormality of the eye is detected or if treatment is required which falls outside the scope of the general ophthalmic services. This includes orthoptic treatment under the health service and the supply of contact lenses under the health service.
3. A satisfactory standard of vision is not achieved even with corrective lenses (no details of the meaning of 'satisfactory' are given).
4. A further examination is required within six months.

### Supply, replacement and repair of spectacles

A contractor must ensure that any prescription for spectacles presented is not more than two years old; this is an amendment to SI 1974/287 introduced by the Health and Social Security Act 1984. When making and supplying an optical appliance the contractor must ensure that all due care and attention is provided. Any optical appliance supplied within the terms of the general ophthalmic services must conform to the styles and quality listed in the relevant schedule.

### Advertising

A contractor may not advertise that his name appears in the list of the FPC or that he provides general ophthalmic services other than by way of the approved notices for display within a practice. The term 'advertising' is meant to include:

1. The issue of circulars or letters.
2. The publication of a notice within any newspaper or other printed paper issued periodically for public circulation.
3. Letter headings and bills.
4. Booklets, leaflets and pamphlets.
5. Canvassing.
6. Public announcements.
7. Display of posters, placards, streamers or signs.
8. Films, slides or announcements at any place of public entertainment.

This particular aspect of the terms of service (i.e. advertising) has been amended to come into line with the new GOC regulations made under the terms of the Health and Social Security Act 1984, allowing unrestricted advertising.

## 3

# Provisions relating to the investigation of NHS disputes, appeals, etc.

**Administration**

In situations in which a contractor is held to have broken the terms of his contract with the family practitioner committee (FPC) there has to be a system by which such action can be investigated. The administrator for such investigations is an officer appointed by the area health authority, who acts as secretary to the FPC. It is the job of each FPC to establish for its area the following service committees to hear such investigations:

1. Medical services committee.
2. Dental services committee.
3. Pharmaceutical services committee.
4. Ophthalmic services committee.
5. Joint services committee.

Of these five, the first and the last are related to ophthalmic services. The membership of the ophthalmic services committee totals 11 and comprises:

1. Chairman.
2. Four lay members appointed by the FPC.
3. Two ophthalmic medical practitioners appointed by the local medical committee.
4. Two ophthalmic opticians appointed by the local optical committee.
5. Two dispensing opticians appointed by the local optical committee.

The membership of the joint services committee also totals 11 but is constituted as follows.

1. Chairman.
2. Two lay members appointed by the FPC.
3. Two medical practitioners from the local medical committee who are also practising doctors.
4. Two dentists appointed by the local dental committee.
5. Two pharmacists appointed by the local pharmaceutical committee.
6. Two ophthalmic members, who may be either ophthalmic medical practitioners or ophthalmic opticians.

## Procedure in complaints

There are regulations concerning the timing of a complaint made against any contractor listed as offering services within the scope of the NHS. In the case of a doctor, pharmacist, ophthalmic medical practitioner or optician, the complaint must be received within eight weeks of the action and a written complaint must have been sent to the Administrator stating the matter to be investigated. If the complaint is received beyond this time limit, the case may still be heard:

1. If the failure in time is due to a reasonable cause.
2. If the service committee obtain the consent of the practitioner, pharmacist or optician involved.
3. If the Secretary of State gives permission.

If consent is not given, the complainant has the right to appeal within 14 days of notification.

If a hearing is to take place then the service committee concerned will permit any person to be assisted in the presentation of his case provided that the assistant takes no active part in the hearing. All initial proceedings are held in private.

The procedure for any investigations to be held is as follows.

1. The Administrator sends a copy of the complainant's statement to the chairman of the relevant committee. If the chairman feels that there has been no breach of the terms of service, the Administrator notifies the complainant who then has 14 days in which to amplify the initial statement. If there is still felt to be no case then the matter is reported to the services committee without a hearing.
2. Where the chairman of the relevant committee considers that there is a case to be answered, the Administrator is instructed to send the statement to the contractor involved for comment. Any comments should be received within four weeks, although this time may be extended if the committee agrees. A copy of these comments, if any, is sent by the Administrator to the complainant for examination, and the complainant is given 14 days to make observations on the comments. This time limit may also be extended if the committee agrees.
3. If the chairman, after examining all the statements and comments, feels that a hearing is no longer necessary then the case may be brought before the relevant service committee for a report without hearing.
4. A hearing is arranged by the Administrator if:
    (a)  the contractor fails to reply;
    (b)  the contractor replies and the chairman feels that there is still a case;
    (c)  there appears to be a material difference between the two statements.
   In this case the Administrator informs both the complainant and the contractor that copies of all documents, including written comments, will be sent to each party. Any such documents will be produced at the hearing, should one be held.
5. If the complaint concerns a deputy then a copy of the documents is also supplied to the deputy, who is treated as if he were a party to the investigation if he applies to the committee to be so treated.

6. If the case relates to a deputy and, in the opinion of the chairman of the committee, the employing party has personally fully complied with the terms of service relating to the provision of services to his patients then a hearing may be dispensed with. If this is the case the dispensing of the hearing does not affect the case against the deputy.
7. The hearing may be postponed by the chairman upon application by either party, provided that the chairman thinks it fit.
8. Seven days before any hearing all members of the service committee and the secretary of the local optical committee involved are sent copies of all documents and statements relating to the case.
9. During the hearing either party is entitled to bring witnesses and, either directly or via the chairman of the committee, to question any witness or involved party.
10. If either party fails to appear at the hearing for any reasonable cause then the hearing may be postponed; before doing so, however, observations may be invited from the party present.
11. If any member of the service committee has an interest in the case, either directly or indirectly, then that member will not take part in the hearing and a deputy must stand in.
12. The chairman of the committee is given a casting vote only and therefore does not normally take part in the voting.
13. If, during the hearing, the complainant introduces any information adding to the original statement, then:
    (a) the chairman may admit or exclude the information;
    (b) if admitted, the hearing may be adjourned;
    (c) if admitted and if the respondent, after consultation, does not wish to adjourn, the chairman may decide to continue.
    If, however, the case is opened before a service committee and the case is subsequently adjourned, the same members must attend the subsequent hearings and no other member of the committee is entitled to be present at any further hearing.
14. The service committee draws up a report stating all the relevant facts as they feel they have been established by the evidence presented, together with a recommendation to the FPC as to the action, if any, which should be taken. If they feel that any breach of the terms of service has occurred then they may draw the attention of the FPC to any previous inquiries and their outcome.
15. A joint services committee inquiry takes the same form except that the quorum required is different.

## Decisions by FPC on committee report

Once the report of a hearing has been sent to the FPC, there are several actions open:

1. The FPC may recommend to the Secretary of State that any expenses incurred by the claimant because of failure by the optician to comply with the terms of service should be stopped from the optician's remuneration and paid back.

2. They may recommend that, because of the optician's failure to comply with his terms of service, an amount should be withheld from his remuneration.
3. If it is felt that the continued inclusion on the relevant list could prove prejudicial to the service in question then the FPC may make representation to a tribunal to that effect.
4. They may recommend to the Secretary of State that a stern warning should be sent indicating that the terms of service must be complied with in the future.

If the FPC decide to take any action which is not recommended by the service committee or which differs from the recommendation of the service committee then adequate reasons must be provided.

## Procedure following FPC decision

As soon as possible after reaching a decision the Administrator furnishes the parties to the investigation and the Secretary of State with a copy of the report and the FPC decision. Also, where appropriate, the right of appeal is notified and the ability of the Secretary of State to furnish costs where considered appropriate.

## Appeals

If an appeal is to be made then it must be sent in writing to the Secretary of State within one month of the receipt of the FPC report. The appeal should contain all the information upon which it is based. Should the Secretary of State decide to hold an oral hearing then he may appoint three members to hear the case; at least one of the members should be of the same profession as the appellant. At the hearing, no new facts may be entered unless they have been presented to the Secretary of State or the person holding the inquiry seven days prior to the date of the hearing. After hearing the case the appeal panel draw up a report and present it to the Secretary of State for consideration. The Secretary of State makes a decision after consideration of the report, and this decision is final.

## FPC investigations of overprescribing

The FPC may investigate overprescribing of optical appliances. The excessive prescribing is measured by reference to the completed forms by all practitioners in the area. If any such case is found then the FPC refer the matter to the ophthalmic services committee. The services committee, before considering the case, must send a statement indicating the facts to be considered to the practitioner involved, giving opportunity for reply. After considering any reply the ophthalmic services committee decides whether or not there was excessive prescribing. If it is proven that the prescribing was beyond that reasonably necessary then the services committee must calculate the cost incurred by the FPC by the excess.

The services committee must then notify the FPC, the practitioner involved and the Secretary of State of their findings and their recommendations. The services committee must also inform the practitioner of his right to appeal within one month of the receipt of their decision. If, after consideration of all the information, the FPC accept the ophthalmic services committee decision that there has been excessive prescribing, they may recommend to the Secretary of State that money be withheld from the optician's remuneration.

In the case of an optician complaining about another optician over a question of the efficiency of the general ophthalmic services offered then the local optical committee may hear the case. This is provided that the complainant is an optician practising in the area of the local committee.

## Tribunals

The final form of hearing with which a practitioner may become involved is the tribunal. A tribunal is set up for hearings involving application for removal of the name of a practitioner from the register or for the reinstatement of a name in the register.

The procedure for a hearing by tribunal is as follows. Representation has to be made in writing, either by or on behalf of the complainant, to the clerk of the tribunal. If, after consideration of this representation, the tribunal think fit, they may request a preliminary statement setting out the alleged facts and the grounds for allegations made. In addition, where facts outside the complainant's personal knowledge are put forward, they must be accompanied by the source of information and the grounds for believing them to be true. Further particulars which might be felt necessary and a statutory declaration verifying the preliminary statement may also be required.

## Tribunal procedure

If the tribunal feel that there are insufficient grounds, except in the case of the complaint being brought by an FPC, they must inform the complainant accordingly. If an inquiry is to be held, however, the clerk sends out the following notices:

1. Form F1 notifying the respondent that it is proposed to hold an inquiry following representation made by the complainant.
2. Form F2 informing the complainant that it is proposed to hold an inquiry and requesting a concise statement (to be made out on Form 2A) of the alleged facts and grounds on which the statement is based, together with a list of all the documents proposed to be used in evidence. A time limit is laid down for this but may be extended at the complainant's request. The tribunal may decide to dispense with the statement on Form 2A if they consider the preliminary statement adequate.
3. The clerk of the tribunal sends the respondent a copy of the statement of complaint and any documents proposed as evidence together with a Form 3 informing the respondent of his right to admit or dispute any or all of the allegations. Any admission or denial must be sent in the form of a written statement to the clerk of the tribunal.

At the discretion of the tribunal, amendments to the statement of complaint will be allowed at any time before the conclusion of inquiry.

The respondent or his agent has the right, upon giving due notice to the complainant, to inspect any document proposed as evidence. It is also permissible, upon application to the clerk of the tribunal, for the respondent to obtain a copy of any such document.

The tribunal appoint a day for the hearing and send out Form 4, not less than 14 days before the inquiry date, to both the complainant and the respondent. If the tribunal think fit, the area FPC may also be notified of the details of the inquiry. The hearing may be postponed upon application to the tribunal by either party.

Should the complainant fail to comply with any of the requirements then the representation may be treated as withdrawn by the tribunal. It is also possible for the complainant to withdraw representation at any time before the inquiry with the consent of the tribunal. In either of the above cases the tribunal informs the respondent of the situation.

Once the inquiry stage is reached the procedure followed is mainly at the discretion of the tribunal. The following provisions, however, are essential.

1. The complainant and respondent may be heard either in person or by another authorised person at the inquiry.
2. The complainant and respondent or their authorised representatives are entitled to call witnesses or produce further evidence at the inquiry.
3. If the tribunal feel that the alleged facts are the subject of a separate tribunal investigation then the proceedings may be suspended to await the outcome of the other investigation.
4. Where the grounds of a representation are based solely on an allegation that the respondent has been convicted of a criminal offence, and the respondent admits the allegation, then the tribunal may, with the consent of the respondent, determine the case solely on documented evidence presented.

At the conclusion of an inquiry the tribunal issue a statement for the Secretary of State, respondent and complainant. This statement contains the findings of fact, the conclusions reached, any directions they suggest and any order they decide to make with regard to costs to the involved parties. The statement is drawn up by the chairman of the tribunal. The Secretary of State forwards copies of the chairman's report to the relevant committees.

The clerk of the tribunal, after the issue of the statement, notifies the respondent in writing of his right to appeal to the Secretary of State against any direction by the tribunal for the removal of his name from the lists. Any appeal made has to be within 14 days and should contain a concise statement of facts and contentions upon which the appellant intends to base his case.

**Appeals against tribunal**

In the case of an appeal the Secretary of State appoints a person to hear the appeal and to report on the matter. Also appointed, to assist the person hearing the appeal, will be someone belonging to the same branch of the health service as the appellant. The appeal may be withdrawn by written notification to the Secretary of State who, upon receipt of notification, confirms the direction of the tribunal. In the case of disqualification the Secretary of State publishes details as he thinks fit.

## Procedure of tribunal for reinstatement hearing

Where a tribunal is set up to hear applications for the reinstatement of a name to the lists the procedure is very similar to that outlined above.

1. An application, by or on behalf of the applicant for reinstatement, is made in writing to the clerk of the tribunal. The application should contain a concise statement of the grounds upon which the application is based, together with a list of documents proposed as evidence.
2. A copy of the application should be sent to the respondent.
3. If the tribunal feel that, after due consideration of the application, there is no need for an inquiry then they may refuse to hold an inquiry and inform the applicant accordingly.
4. If the tribunal decide to hold an inquiry then the applicant and respondent are notified accordingly.
5. Notification of the date, the time and the venue of any hearing is sent to the respondent and applicant at least 14 days before the proposed hearing.
6. Upon written notification the applicant may withdraw, provided the tribunal consent.
7. Any inquiry should be held in camera unless the applicant has applied for a public hearing.
8. The respondent has the right to inspect any documents proposed as evidence.
9. The applicant and the respondent have the right to be represented at the hearing.
10. A report of the findings is drawn up by the chairman of the tribunal, indicating the action suggested as in the previous procedure.

# 4

# Opticians Act 1958

Members of the ophthalmic profession attempted to obtain legislation to establish and control their profession from the early 1900s. It seemed that, when the optical bodies had given evidence on the scheme for optical benefits to the Royal Commission considering the National Health Insurance Acts, there was a possibility that legislation would be forthcoming. In 1926 the Joint Council of Qualified Opticians drafted a non-prohibitive Bill to recognise opticians with an approved certificate or who had been in practice for at least five years before the proposed Optical Practitioners (Registration) Bill and who had also passed a practical examination.

Sponsorship for the Bill was provided by Mr West Russell and the first reading took place in February 1927. Before the second reading took place in May 1927 the Ministry of Health instituted a departmental inquiry into the optical aspects of the Bill. The Departmental Committee consisted of three ophthalmic opticians, three medical men, two members appointed by the Ministry and four lay members, under the chairmanship of Sir Frank Boyd Merriman. The terms of reference for this Committee were:

'to consider the Optical Practitioners (Registration) Bill and to make recommendations'.

Because of the Departmental Inquiry the Bill itself failed its second reading in May 1927.

The result of the inquiry published at the end of 1927 was disappointing for the optical profession. A majority report was issued signed by nine members, a first minority report signed by the three ophthalmic opticians and a second minority report signed by an MP. The main stumbling block seemed to comprise the lack of consistency in training and amongst the examining bodies and, in particular, the training in the recognition of ocular disease. The result was that the Bill was not resubmitted for consideration. Although the majority report did say that reconsideration would be possible if the ophthalmic service failed, it took 22 years for that reconsideration to take place.

It was following the introduction of the 1946 National Health Service Act that the Minister of Health in 1949 set up an Interdepartmental Committee under the chairmanship of Lord Crook. The terms of reference of this Committee were to:

'advise, on the assumption that it would be in the public interest that provision should be made by legislation for the registration of opticians, how registration could best be carried out, and what qualifications should be required as a condition of registration.'

The Committee consisted of 13 members, comprising ophthalmic opticians, dispensing opticians, ophthalmologists, members of the medical profession, a physicist, a physiologist, a member of the teaching profession and a member of the general public.

Early in 1952 the Committee published a unanimous report in which they recommended that legislation should provide:

1. For the establishment of a body to be known as the General Optical Council which would set up and maintain appropriate registers of opticians.
2. That all opticians recognised by the National Health Service Act 1946 should be eligible for registration but that all future applicants would be required to possess a qualification from one of the recognised optical bodies.
3. That the General Optical Council should exercise disciplinary power over registered opticians and have power to admit, remove and restore names to the registers and that they should maintain an appropriate ethical standard.
4. That the General Optical Council should organise inspections of optical examining bodies and of the optical training institutions.
5. That ophthalmic opticians and ophthalmic optical students should receive more training from medical men (*sic*) in certain subjects and be allowed to have further clinical training by medical men in appropriate hospital departments.

This set of recommendations was obviously a tremendous step forward but, despite pressure from a number of parties, the Minister of Health failed, after repeated promises, to introduce the Bill. It was left until 1957 when it was presented as a Private Member's Bill* by the Member for Wembley South, Mr Ronald Russell. The Bill passed speedily through the Houses and received Royal Assent in the House of Lords on 7 July 1958.

## Purpose of the Opticians Act 1958

The Opticians Act 1958 was enacted:

'to provide for the registration of opticians and the enrolment of bodies corporate carrying on business as opticians; to regulate the practice of

---

* Private Member's Bill. This is a Public Bill which is introduced by a private member of the House of Commons instead of by the Government. A total of 10 days in each parliamentary session are allocated to Private Members' Bills and it is therefore very difficult for such measures to become law; they may, however, become adopted by the Government or stir up enough controversy to instigate an inquiry.

opticians and the conduct by such bodies corporate of their business as opticians; to impose restrictions on the testing of sight and the supply of optical appliances; and for the purposes connected therewith'.

## Establishment of the General Optical Council

Section 1 of the Opticians Act 1958 established a General Optical Council (GOC) whose function was to promote high standards of professional education and conduct. The Council comprised according to the Schedule:

1. Four members appointed by the Privy Council*.
2. Five representatives of registered ophthalmic opticians.
3. Two representatives of registered dispensing opticians.
4. Six members nominated by examining bodies.
5. Six registered medical practitioners.
6. One member nominated by the Governor of Northern Ireland.

## Primary duties of the GOC

It was the first duty of the GOC to set up three registers of opticians:

1. A register of ophthalmic opticians engaged only in the testing of sight.
2. A register of ophthalmic opticians engaged in the testing of sight and in the fitting and supply of optical appliances.
3. A register of dispensing opticians.

The qualifications required for inclusion in the register were also laid down, but no optician can be included in more than one list even with qualifications entitling inclusion in more than one. These qualifications were included in the register, together with name, address and such other particulars as might be prescribed by the Council.

The GOC also established a register of bodies corporate carrying on business as ophthalmic opticians and a further register of bodies corporate carrying on business as dispensing opticians. The lists contained the names, principal place of business and such other particulars as might be prescribed.

In connection with the maintenance of these lists the GOC:

1. Control applications for registration.
2. Require notification of changes in the particulars shown in the lists.
3. Prescribe an annual fee for registration.
4. Register additional qualifications.
5. May refuse to enter or maintain a name if the registration fee is not paid.
6. Record the death of registered opticians.
7. Publish annually either registers and lists or amendments to the existing registers.

---

* Privy Council. The main function of this body is to give formal effect to Proclamations and Orders of Council. Members of the Council include Cabinet Ministers, two archbishops and other leading statesmen and stateswomen. Only a small number of Privy Councillors are invited to attend Council meetings and normally it would be those members with special interest in the matters to be dealt with.

The approval of training institutions and qualifications and their supervision are carried out by the GOC as laid down in ss. 5 and 6 of the Opticians Act 1958.

Section 30(2) of the Act defines the testing of sight as:

'Testing sight with the object of determining whether there is any and, if so, what defect of sight and of correcting, remedying or relieving any such defect of an anatomical or physiological nature by means of an optical appliance prescribed on the basis of determination.'

This function is restricted to:

1. Registered medical practitioners.
2. Registered ophthalmic opticians.
3. Medical students.
4. Persons training as ophthalmic opticians who are exempted under the GOC regulations.

The six institutions offering a qualification acceptable to the GOC regarding item 4, above, are:

Aston University
Bradford University
City University
Glasgow College of Technology
University of Manchester Institute of Science & Technology
University of Wales Institute of Science and Technology.

Following the successful pursuance of the approved course at any of the above institutions, one is required to obtain a further qualification before registration on one of the lists approved by the GOC. This further registerable qualification was, until 1980, one of the following:

1. Fellowship Diploma of the British Optical Association.
2. Fellowship in Ophthalmic Optics of the Worshipful Company of Spectacle Makers.
3. Fellowship Diploma of the Scottish Association of Opticians.

However, the British College of Ophthalmic Opticians (Optometrists) has now been set up, and the new qualification approved by the GOC for registration is MBCO.

## Sale and supply of optical appliances

Section 21 of the Opticians Act 1958 relates to the sale and supply of optical appliances, and prohibited the sale of any optical appliance unless under the supervision of a registered medical practitioner or registered optician. The exceptions to this regulation were where:

1. The sale was made to a registered medical practitioner, registered optician or enrolled body corporate for the purpose of his practice or of his or its business.
2. The sale was made to a manufacturer of, or a dealer in, optical appliances for the purpose of his business.

3. The sale was to any authority or person carrying on a hospital, clinic, nursing home or other institution providing medical or surgical treatment.
4. The sale was to a Minister of the Crown or government department.
5. The sale was for the purpose of export.
6. The appliance was sold as an antique or second-hand article.

Section 21, however, has recently come under fire from the Government and, under the terms of the Health and Social Security Act 1984, has been repealed. This is discussed in more detail in Chapter 5.


## Use of recognised titles

The Opticians Act 1958 prohibits, under s. 22, the use of particular titles. An individual is liable to a fine if he:

1. Takes or uses any of the following titles (either alone or in combination with any other words): 'ophthalmic optician' when he is not in either of the registers of ophthalmic opticians; or 'dispensing optician' when he is not in the register of dispensing opticians; or 'registered optician' or 'enrolled optician' when he is not registered in any of the registers.
2. Takes or uses any name, title, addition or description falsely implying, or otherwise pretends, that he is registered in any of the registers.

   This section, like s. 21, has been modified by the Health and Social Security Act 1984, in which the title 'optometrist' is included as a protected title.


## Additional powers for the GOC

Under s. 25, the Opticians Act 1958 empowers the GOC to make rules prohibiting or regulating:

1. The use by registered opticians and enrolled bodies corporate of any means of giving publicity, whether by advertisement or not, to their practice or business of ophthalmic or dispensing opticians.
2. The carrying on of practice or business by registered opticians and enrolled bodies corporate under names other than those under which they are registered or enrolled.
3. The administration of drugs by registered opticians, enrolled bodies corporate and their employees in the course of their practice or business of ophthalmic or dispensing opticians.
4. The practise of orthoptics by registered opticians, enrolled bodies corporate and their employees.
5. The prescription, supply and fitting of contact lenses by registered opticians, enrolled bodies corporate and their employees.

   Subsection 3 of s. 25 placed the further task on the GOC of making and submitting rules to the Privy Council providing that, where it appears to a registered optician that a person consulting him is suffering from an injury or disease of the eye, the optician should take prescribed steps to refer that person to a registered medical practitioner for advice and treatment.

## Present composition and scope of the GOC

It can be seen from the above that the main purpose of the Opticians Act 1958 was to lay down the basis for the establishment and general function of the GOC. Since the initial steps, the GOC has become very firmly established. The membership of 25, each member having a term of office of five years, comprises:

1. Seven members nominated by the Privy Council, one of whom is to be the chairman. Of these seven, four are lay members, two are doctors and one an educationalist.
2. One lay member appointed by the Secretary of State for Northern Ireland.
3. Four ophthalmologists nominated by the Faculty of Ophthalmologists (one representing Scotland).
4. Four members nominated by the British College of Ophthalmic Opticians (Optometrists).
5. One member nominated by the Association of Dispensing Opticians.
6. One member nominated jointly by the six approved training institutions.
7. Five members elected by registered ophthalmic opticians.
8. Two members elected by registered dispensing opticians.

## Regulations regarding publicity

Regulations relating to publicity were approved by the Privy Council in April 1964. These rules were revised and updated to take effect from 1 May 1981, when the general rule required that all publicity be of a dignified and restrained character and free from any reference to the efficiency of, or the facilities given by, other registered opticians or enrolled bodies corporate. Except for this general rule, there was no restriction on publicity in trade or professional press.

The use of reminders by registered opticians was permissible provided that the following rules were observed:

1. The reminder was either that a further sight test was desirable, and was sent to a person who had previously had an eye examination within the practice, or that an appliance fitted might need adjustment.
2. It was felt that, in the registered optician's professional judgement, an eye examination or adjustment of the appliance was necessary.
3. The reminder was by personal communication.

A registered optician or enrolled body corporate might send to patients who had had their eyes examined or been supplied with an optical appliance, details of:

1. Change in address of the practice.
2. Change in telephone number of the practice.
3. Closing of the premises.
4. Change in the hours of opening of the premises.
5. Change of the name under which the practice or business is carried on.
6. Acquisition of goodwill of a practice or business.
7. Transfer of the goodwill to another registered optician or enrolled body corporate.

8. Change in partners within a practice or directors in a body corporate.
9. Transfer of name from one register or list to another.
10. The opening of new premises likely to be more conveniently accessible to that person than the practice previously visited.
11. Any error or omission in a Post Office telephone directory.
12. Any special event which may be approved by the Council.

The regulations also allowed for a registered optician to supply booklets, leaflets or pamphlets relating to optical appliances or visual welfare to patients either by making them available at the practice or by sending them to patients who had had an eye examination or been supplied with an optical appliance. It was also not an offence to send the information to any person who had specifically requested it.

If a registered optician was involved in other business then all displays of optical appliances, accessories, sunglasses and optical instruments visible from outside the premises had to be separated from displays of any other article for sale.

There were certain exemptions to the rule on publicity and, provided the notice was of a dignified and restrained character, a practitioner or enrolled body corporate might:

1. Make any statement, announcement or advertisement required by or under any statutory provisions.
2. Advertise to obtain staff, accommodation or equipment.
3. Advertise details of purchase or sale of goodwill, premises, equipment or other assets of a practice or business.
4. Be referred to in an article incidental to an item of current news which was not designed to give publicity to a practice or business.
5. Be referred to in items pertaining to an election in which the practitioner was a candidate, provided it was not designed to give publicity to a practice or business.
6. Be included in the text of a telephone directory, street directory or the like, provided there was no prominence over other details.

The main change in the publicity regulations imposed by the GOC in 1981 was that

'there was to be no advertising of any sort in the general press'.

The Health and Social Security Act 1984 introduced changes in the procedure of the GOC as regards regulating advertising, which has resulted in new regulations as outlined in Chapter 5.

## GOC regulations on drugs

As regards professional practice, the GOC has made the following recommendations concerning the use of drugs.

1. The need for care and discrimination in the use of drugs is emphasised, and any demonstration that indiscriminate or irresponsible use of drugs has occurred could lead to disciplinary action.
2. In the 'Notice for the Guidance of the Profession', N18, published by the GOC (1981) there seems to have been a subtle change in the regulations

as regards the use of drugs. In previous notices there was a clause indicating that a registered optician would not be considered as failing in his duty if he tested sight without the use of drugs.

This clause was, however, omitted from N18, and this suggests that the use of drugs is becoming more necessary for adequate provision of general ophthalmic services.

3. With respect to the treatment of injury or disease of the eye, only first aid treatment in emergencies may be undertaken if such action appears necessary in the interests of the injured person.
4. Any rights under alternative qualifications do not fall within the Council's restrictions.

## GOC recommendations and regulations on fitting of contact lenses

Prior to the publication of N18 by the GOC the following regulations—guidelines were proposed for contact lens fitting.

'The fitting of contact lenses by practitioners is controlled by the General Optical Council. It is felt that the present university training in ophthalmic optics covers the required theoretical basis, but that further work after qualification is necessary to achieve a proficient standard. Although no registered optician is barred from contact lens fitting, irrespective of experience, it is suggested that any optician undertaking fitting should take a post-qualifying course; this is particularly relevant in cases where the old syllabus provided initial qualification.'

The Council will, in the case of specially qualified practitioners, allow annotation of the name in the register. If annotation is allowed then such opticians may use the titles:

1. Contact lens practitioner, if an ophthalmic optician.
2. Contact lens fitter, if a dispensing optician.

These descriptions may be used at their practice address and on notepaper.

Where a dispensing optician undertakes the fitting of contact lenses, the following procedure should be followed.

1. An instruction to supply lenses, including a recent spectacle correction and other relevant details, is needed from an ophthalmologist, or an ophthalmic medical practitioner or an ophthalmic optician.
2. The accuracy during the making and fitting of contact lenses may be checked, but this will not constitute the right to test sight within the meaning of the Opticians Act 1958.
3. On completion of the fitting, the patient must be instructed to return to the original prescriber and the dispensing optician must notify the prescriber in writing that this has been done.

Since the publication of N18 the situation has changed, and the GOC now feel that contact lens practice can be adequately controlled under the recommendations embodied in section 78 of N18, which states that for the protection of both the individual patient and the public at large, all registered opticians are expected to maintain the highest possible standards of experience, training, performance and behaviour in all of their professional activities.

It seems that legislation on contact lenses is no nearer, despite the provision of s. 25 (1)(e) of the Opticians Act which states that the GOC may make rules prohibiting or regulating

'the prescription, supply and fitting by registered opticians, enrolled bodies corporate and their employees of contact lenses'

and a report from an ad hoc committee set up by the GOC to study the problems.

The recommendations of the ad hoc committee in the form of draft rules were circulated and, on the basis of comments received, a final report was submitted to the GOC in 1980 which recommended that it was unnecessary for the protection of the public to regulate, by statutory rule, contact lens practice. The draft rules themselves contained restriction on those qualified to undertake contact lens practice and details of what was necessary to undertake a contact lens fitting.

The GOC made a further attempt to introduce 'Contact Lens Rules' in 1984 but this time the Privy Council decided that, under the terms of the Opticians Act 1958, the GOC could only offer guidance. With this in mind the GOC have now introduced guidance in the form of Notices N20 and N21.

Notice N20 advises that failing to make adequate arrangements for continuing clinical care of patients fitted with contact lenses could be considered serious professional misconduct by the Disciplinary Committee of the GOC. If a patient refuses to return for supervised aftercare then that fact should be recorded on the patient's record.

Notice N21 is made to accompany the General Optical Council (Rules on Fitting Contact Lenses) Order of Council (SI 1985/856) which state that certain categories of optician may fit contact lenses for training purposes provided that fitting is carried out under the continuous personal supervision of a registered optician or registered medical practitioner. Notice N20 itself details those groups which are classified as trainees for the purpose of fitting contact lenses within the terms of the Rules on Fitting Contact Lenses 1985.

### GOC and disease or injury to the eye

Statutory Instrument 1960/1936 embodies the rules laid down by the GOC covering injury or disease of the eye. The regulations state that:

1. If a patient attending a registered optician appears to be suffering from an injury or disease of the eye, of which the patient's general practitioner may be unaware, then the registered optician shall report any findings to the practitioner.
2. The following procedure should be adhered to:
   (a) advise the patient to consult a medical practitioner;
   (b) wherever possible, a written report of findings, indicating the grounds for thinking that injury or disease of the eye is present, is sent to a registered medical practitioner named by the patient;

(c) if action appears urgent, then such measures as are available to inform the registered medical practitioner immediately are taken.
3. If a patient who appears to be suffering from injury or disease of the eye is unwilling to consult a registered medical practitioner on conscientious or other grounds, then the optician must record that fact and the grounds given.
4. None of the regulations regarding referral will prevent any optician from rendering, in an emergency, whatever services are in the best interests of the person consulting him.

## Professional conduct

As in all professions, certain standards of conduct are expected of registered opticians, and the GOC offer the following.

1. Any secrets of a personal nature relating to professional services rendered, entrusted to an optician's care, will remain inviolate.
2. It is illegal to dispense prescriptions for optical appliances issued in contravention of the law.
3. Registered opticians and enrolled bodies corporate should not display membership certificates, diplomas and the like in the windows of their premises.
4. It is undesirable for a registered optician or an enrolled body corporate to offer any discount arrangement covering the testing of sight or the fitting and supply of optical appliances.
5. All contact with the press should be of a restrained and completely professional nature.

## Committees of the GOC

Under the Opticians Act, the GOC was specifically required to establish certain committees. It was to be the function of the Education Committee to advise on all matters relating to optical training and examinations. It was to include one person representing those training ophthalmic opticians, one person representing those training dispensing opticians and one person nominated by the Minister of Education, the other members to be appointed by the GOC as set out in the Opticians Act 1958. The Companies Committee was established to offer advice on matters (other than disciplinary) relating to bodies corporate carrying on business as ophthalmic or dispensing opticians. It was to include one member representative of bodies corporate carrying on business as ophthalmic opticians and one member representative of bodies corporate carrying on business as dispensing opticians. The other members were to be appointed by the GOC as laid down in the Opticians Act 1958.

## Opticians Act (Amendment) Bill

Since the introduction of the Opticians Act 1958 there have been pressures from commercial and political sources to alter some of the details of the Opticians Act 1958. The restrictions of certain functions to be carried out only by qualified persons seems to be against the general principles or interests of some groups and this conflict has led to two major recent developments. One of these is the Office of Fair Trading Report 1982; the other is the attempted introduction of a Bill, the Opticians Act (Amendment) Bill by Lord Rugby in 1982.

It was Lord Rugby's contention that s. 21 of the Opticians Act 1958 was too prohibitive. It states that:

> 'Subject to the following provisions of this section, a person shall not sell any optical appliances unless the sale is effected by or under the supervision of a registered medical practitioner or registered optician.'

Taking up the case put forward by an American company which wished to sell spectacles 'over the counter' and without the need for eye examination or qualified fitting, Lord Rugby suggested that it was in the public interest to have this open market approach. The major public advantage seems to have been seen as the cost of such spectacles. The proposal received support from some quarters and it is strange how the issues which had so rapidly carried through the original 1958 legislation (i.e. the advantages of screening and adequate qualified eye care) are now seen by some as totally unnecessary when, in terms of volume of patients and pressure on hospital services, the ophthalmic profession is probably even more in demand.

The legislation passed its first reading and was given a second airing in the House of Lords on 18 February 1982. At this stage, when it was likely that the Bill would have been defeated if it had gone to vote, Lord Rugby withdrew the paper because of the Government inquiry being undertaken by the Director General of the Office of Fair Trading. This left the way open for the Government to take stock of the situation and draft their Health and Social Security Bill.

# 5

# Health and Social Security Act 1984

In the last three years there has been an upsurge in public awareness of spectacle costs but not in the professional service. Pressure has been mounting for changes in the general ophthalmic services; the pressure has come from consumer groups, from commercial concerns and as a result of financial cutbacks within the NHS. The first thrust, as has been mentioned in Chapter 4, was an attempt to introduce, through the House of Lords, the Opticians Act (Amendment) Bill 1982. The major aim of this legislation was to introduce over-the-counter sales of reading spectacles on the grounds that it would reduce spectacle costs. The Bill was sponsored by Lord Rugby and followed independent representation by commercial optical companies for the easing of regulations. The Bill passed its first reading but was withdrawn following a Government undertaking to direct the Office of Fair Trading to investigate the supply of optical services within the UK. Weight was added to the need for such an investigation by reports from consumer groups suggesting, incorrectly, that spectacle prices in the UK were very much higher than elsewhere, and that optical services could be improved by the introduction of competition – this despite showing that prices already ranged by more than £30 for a similar item.

The Office of Fair Trading published its report, *Opticians and Competition*, in December 1982. The report concluded that although opticians did not make undue profits there were certain measures which would, in their opinion, improve the service to the public. The main improvement would be the introduction of competition into the supply of spectacles by removal of the professional 'monopoly' on spectacle supplies. Coupled with this, greater freedom to advertise would offer greater choice and wider information to the public when considering spectacles.

The Government used the Office of Fair Trading report to draw up a Bill with much greater scope than had been previously imagined. In fact, a Bill with such far-reaching consequences that many of the organisations which had originally pressed for changes in the legislation now campaigned against the new measures. The Bill as a whole was designed to amend or supplement existing legislation regarding: optical services and the optical profession; the status and constitution of family practitioner committees; finance within the health service; disablement allowances; social security benefits; occupational pension schemes and membership of social security appeal panels. Whilst the general eye examination was left untouched in the new legislation on the grounds that a necessary service of screening was met by ophthalmic opticians/optometrists, the supply of spectacles and the regulations governing the practice of optometry and the provisions of the health service have all been radically altered. It must be said that similar provisions appeared in the USA some years ago and the situation has now resolved itself such that the optometric profession is well established. The major difference in the UK is that the cost of eye examinations here is fixed by the Government at £8.60 per patient, which is far lower than in other countries.

The Health and Social Security Act 1984, as can be seen from the foregoing, was introduced to cover a wide range of diverse legislation. It is Part I of the Act which is of particular importance to the ophthalmic/ optometric and dispensing professions. It deals with amendments to existing legislation such as the Opticians Act 1958 as well as the introduction of new legislative control. The first change proposed by the Act is amendment of s. 21 of the Opticians Act 1958 concerning the supply of optical appliances. The aim of this amendment is to remove the monopoly held by the profession. The full details of this change were not known until publication of the relevant statutory instruments two months after the original Act had been passed. Basically the supply of spectacles to the public is open to anyone whether or not they hold an optical qualification. There are certain exemptions from this general principle such as the supply of appliances to children under the age of 16 years and to the registered blind or partially sighted, and these are fully detailed in the subsequent Orders of Council SI 1984/1778 and SI 1985/298.

This amendment, which may at the first glance appear to be a reasonable step for the introduction of competition and reduction in prices, is not quite as straightforward as it seems. At present the supply of private spectacles is used by the optometric profession to subsidise the eye examination fee. The qualified professional requires equipment for both the eye examination and dispensing under his terms of registration, but the unqualified does not have these same constraints and it will therefore become difficult to compete directly. If the sale of spectacles moves from the qualified to the unqualified then this source of subsidy is lost, which will presumably result in poorer facilities for the eye examination. It seems that in their desire to open up the market the Government have actually made competition by the qualified more difficult. One aspect which has not changed is that, despite opening up the regulations to allow the sale of appliances by the unregistered, the Government still have not allowed over-the-counter sales of ready-glazed appliances.

In order to 'control' the unregistered selling introduced by this legislation the Privy Council, by the powers given under the terms of the Opticians Act 1958, have produced SI 1984/1778, The Sale of Optical Appliances Order of Council. The order came into effect on 10 December 1984. Under the new terms, anyone even without qualification is allowed to supply spectacle frames provided that such frames contain no cellulose nitrate or celluloid. Lenses can also be supplied provided they are to a valid prescription signed by a registered ophthalmic optician/optometrist or registered ophthalmic medical practitioner and provided that the prescription is not more than two years old. All spectacles must conform to clauses 6–12 of British Standard 2738:1985 referring to tolerance and quality. In addition to these general requirements there are further conditions relating to 'complex' spectacles. For the purpose of SI 1984/1778, 'complex' spectacles are defined as appliances other than those which are:

1. Prescribed for near vision only.
2. Single vision spherical lenses.
3. Appliances having positive power lenses not exceeding 5.00 D.

The 'complex' spectacles are required:

1. To be verified by focimeter as being in accordance with the written prescription.
2. To have the lenses centred by reference to the patient's interpupillary distance.
3. To have an allowance incorporated to take account of any specified back vertex distance.

Section 1(2) of the Health and Social Security Act 1984 amends s. 25 of the Opticians Act 1958 regarding the GOC's regulatory function on advertising. The debate prior to the new legislation and the Government's comments in general showed that a more relaxed attitude to advertising by the profession was favoured. The GOC were unable to offer regulations which suited these attitudes on advertising and therefore a subtle but important amendment was introduced in the new Health and Social Security Act 1984 to cover this. Under the terms of the Opticians Act 1958 the GOC made draft regulations on advertising which were sent to the Privy Council for approval before implementation; if at this stage the Privy Council were not satisfied with the regulations, they were sent back to the GOC for redrafting. Under the new terms the GOC will again be expected to make draft regulations for submission to the Privy Council but if, at this stage, the Privy Council are not satisfied then they may change the regulations themselves even without the consent of the GOC although parliamentary agreement would be required. In this situation the opinion of a government-established body – the GOC – whose membership is drawn from the optometric profession, the dispensing profession, the ophthalmological profession, the civil service and educationalists and includes lay representation could be ignored in favour of a group which may have no specialist knowledge of the subject. If the change in drafting by the Privy Council were approved by the GOC then the regulation would automatically be introduced.

It is possible that this amendment will have little effect on the rules and regulations regarding advertising; on the other hand, the potential is there for the Privy Council to make a political decision totally against the specialist body established by Parliament to take such decisions. The GOC was formed as a non-political regulatory body to monitor the professions and to protect the public; the optometric profession does not hold and has never held a majority on the Council and is not therefore likely to be able to introduce self-interest regulations. As it happens, the Privy Council have already used their new power to overturn the GOC's regulations and substitute their own.

These new 'draft' guidelines, called the Rules on Publicity 1984, are now part of SI 1985/203; s. 3 states:

'A registered optician or an enrolled body corporate shall not use:
'(a) in relation to his or its practice or business, a means of giving publicity which is not legal, decent, honest or truthful, or which is of a character that could reasonably be regarded as likely to bring the profession of ophthalmic optics or of dispensing optics into disrepute or which contains any reference to the efficiency of, or the facilities given by, other registered opticians or enrolled bodies corporate;
'(b) in relation to his or its practice or business a means of giving publicity which makes a claim not capable of substantiation, or a claim which suggests superiority over any other practice or business.'

The latter parts of s. 1 of the Health and Social Security Act 1984 relate to the arrangements for the supply of appliances within the scope of the NHS and to the payment of or contributions towards the costs of appliances. The effect was to withdraw availability of NHS spectacles and lenses from 1 April 1985 other than to exempt groups – children aged under 16 years, people with a defined financial need and other specific persons listed in SI 1985/298. For the purpose of these Amendment Regulations the term 'complex' lens is defined as any lens having a power in any one meridian of plus or minus 10 dioptres or more; this is not to be confused with the term 'complex' spectacles contained in Order of Council SI 1984/1778.

At a later date it is proposed that the complete range of NHS appliances will be withdrawn from all patients, and a voucher system introduced to help those in financial need to offset the cost of spectacles. This measure is intended to save several million pounds on the present health service budget. The removal of the option of health service appliances has greatly upset many consumer groups who feel that, despite the moves to open up competition, they will now pay more for their spectacles because of removal of government subsidy.

Section 2 of the 1984 Act inserts one complete section and two subsections into s. 25 of the Opticians Act 1958. All of the amendments relate to the fitting of contact lenses. The regulations prohibit the fitting of contact lenses by persons other than registered medical practitioners and registered opticians. It also empowers the GOC to specify the qualifications required by registered opticians, and accordingly Notice N21 was issued by the Council to enable trainee opticians to fit lenses.

Section 3 amends s. 22 of the Opticians Act 1958, regarding the protection of titles. In the original Opticians Act 1958 the titles 'ophthalmic optician' and 'dispensing optician' were protected and could be used only by persons registered in the relevant GOC lists. The Health and Social Security Act 1984 amends this section and includes for the first time protection of the title 'optometrist'; whilst this is a step forward, removal of protection of the term 'optician' must be seen as a retrograde step. Under the terms of the new legislation, any person selling optical appliances, whether he/she holds a relevant qualification or not, is entitled to use the title 'optician'. The unregistered and unqualified can use the term 'optician' either on its own or in combination with other terms (e.g. consultant, unqualified, specialist) provided that it does not imply that they are registered in the GOC lists. The total impact of this will not be fully appreciated until publication of the statutory instruments, which it is hoped may carry some modification to the above proposals.

Two further sections of the 1984 Act affect the practice of optometry in the UK: s.4 deals with disciplinary powers of the GOC and s.5 with the constitution of FPCs which administer the NHS at local level.

Section 4 again amends the Opticians Act 1958, this time extending the disciplinary powers of the GOC. In addition to the power to remove registration of practitioners as laid down in the Opticians Act 1958, the GOC may now suspend registration or impose financial penalties on practitioners who do not comply with the regulations. It is hoped that this greater freedom of action may encourage the Council to take action against lesser offences which, until the present legislation, could not be sensibly dealt with.

Section 5 provides for changes in the status and constitution of FPCs. It was the Health Services and Public Health Act 1968 which first gave the ophthalmic and dispensing professions representation on the local administrative bodies, then called executive councils but later renamed the family practitioner committees. This was to coincide with the ophthalmic services becoming a permanent part of the health service. The 1984 Act now makes provision to remove the representation of dispensing opticians on the FPC, the place created by such a move to be filled by one person chosen from nominations by the local medical, dental, pharmaceutical and optical committees. The exact date on which this is to come into effect is not yet known but the principle is obviously a blow to the dispensing profession.

These then are the various measures passed by Parliament and which came into effect on 1 October 1984, and to be administered by subsequent statutory intruments. The legislation has gone through despite widespread concern expressed by numerous organisations, both professional and consumer.

The effect on the general public will be, according to government reports, a beneficial reduction in the cost of optical appliances produced by the increased competition. The difficulty is that the profession feel that a reduction in cost will be brought about by a reduction in standard of aids supplied with the unregistered using poorer quality control. In addition, a loss of fees from supply of spectacles will mean that the registered optician either will have to charge more for his services, thus increasing the cost to the patient, or will have to increase the patient throughput, thereby reducing the amount of time spent with each patient and lowering the overall standard of eye care, both of which are against the patient's best interests.

Moreover, the removal of the health-service-dispensed alternatives and subsequent government subsidy will mean that those patients with more specialised requirements will now find themselves paying considerably more despite the free competition. It may even lead to the prescribing of inferior and inaccurate corrections in an attempt to reduce the costs to the patient.

The effect on the optometric profession in the UK is likely to be dramatic in the short term, and the introduction of large chains of fashion boutiques and unqualified suppliers is foreseen. The monitoring provisions to control the non-professionals are at best inadequate and in many instances non-existent, whilst those regulations monitoring the registered professional have been tightened, placing the qualified practitioner at a distinct disadvantage.

It remains to be seen whether the public generally will retain loyalty to the practitioner who offers a professional, caring and total eye care service, albeit at a slightly higher cost, or will flock to the market place for their optical appliances. The situation is obviously going to change the attitude of the professional practitioner. This may prove a blessing in disguise if the right lessons are learned quickly enough. There is a greater need for publicity of the professional aspects of optometry on a national basis rather than on an independent practitioner basis and a need for better awareness of the patient's requirements.

# 6

# General Optical Council disciplinary procedures

The NHS regulations regarding ophthalmic practice and the general investigation procedures have been dealt with in Chapters 2 and 3. There is a further disciplinary process, however, which is governed by the GOC. Although the two may well interact, they have different outcomes. The NHS procedures relate to a contractor having broken the terms of service for practitioners as laid down in the relevant statutory instruments; the GOC procedures are much more far reaching and can relate to anything which may relate to the practitioner in an ophthalmic practice situation. The outcome of the two procedures is also different in that the NHS investigation may result in prohibition to practise within the health service whilst the GOC investigation may result in erasure of the practitioner's name from the lists and total prohibition to practise.

## Scope of GOC discipline

As laid down in ss. 9–16 of the Opticians Act 1958 and regulated by SIs 1960/1934, 1960/1935, 1961/1239 and 1961/1933, the GOC have the right to investigate any breach of professional discipline. In this connection there are two committees, established under the Opticians Act 1958: the Investigating Committee carries out the preliminary investigation, and the Disciplinary Committee considers and decides sufficiently serious disciplinary cases referred to them by the Investigating Committee. In the case of a decision by the Disciplinary Committee to strike the name of a registered optician from the register, there exists the right of appeal against the decision, to the Judicial Committee of the Privy Council.

The disciplinary jurisdiction covers the following offences.

1. A criminal offence, other than a trivial one, by a registered optician.
2. Infamous conduct in any professional respect by a registered optician.
3. Any offence by a body corporate under the terms of the Opticians Act 1958.
4. Failure by a body corporate to observe the required conditions of enrolment.
5. Connivance by a body corporate at conduct leading to the erasure from the register of the name of a registered optician in its employ.

6. Breach of the rules made under s. 25 of the Opticians Act 1958 relating to:
   (a) publicity;
   (b) the name under which business is carried out;
   (c) the administering of drugs;
   (d) the prescription, supply and fitting of contact lenses.
7. Failure to make adequate arrangements for the fitting and supply of optical appliances.
8. Entries in a register or list made on fraudulent or incorrect grounds.

## Composition of the Investigating Committee

The Investigating Committee has no special procedure laid down and ordinary committee procedure applies. At present the Chairman of the GOC may not be a member of this committee. The Committee is made up of six members of the Council, two of whom are lay members, one an ophthalmologist, two representatives of ophthalmic opticians and one representative of dispensing opticians. If the dispensing representative declares an interest in a particular case then his place on the Committee is taken by either an ophthalmologist or a lay member of the Council. If the case is to be against a body corporate then the committee may co-opt either an ophthalmic representative or a dispensing representative of corporate bodies, depending upon the allegation.

## Procedure for the Investigating Committee

A brief outline of the general procedure is as follows.

The Registrar of the GOC receives a complaint that a registered optician has committed a disciplinary offence. The complainant is required to supply one or more statutory declarations concerning the offence. The whole matter is then referred to the Chairman of the Investigating Committee, who decides whether to deal with the matter in some alternative way. In the case of a Committee meeting being called, documentary evidence only is considered; there is no formal examination of witnesses or oral evidence. Although all parties are entitled to submit observations, no one is entitled to be present during the Committee's deliberations. It is the function of the Committee, when so called upon, to decide whether the case is sufficiently serious to be referred to the Disciplinary Committee.

## Composition of the Disciplinary Committee

The Disciplinary Committee, like the Investigating Committee, has its constitution decided by the GOC. The Chairman of the Council acts as Chairman of the Disciplinary Committee. The other members should include the GOC general medical practitioner nominated by the Privy Council, two of the GOC lay members appointed by the Privy Council or the Secretary of State for Northern Ireland, two ophthalmologists, four representatives of ophthalmic opticians and two representatives of dispensing opticians; if possible, there should be at least one member resident in each of Scotland, Wales and Northern Ireland. No person who has been on the Investigating Committee for a particular case may also sit in the Disciplinary Committee for that case. Although provision is made for 12 members, it is only necessary for a total of five to take part in the proceedings, and there is no restriction on which five members may take part.

## Procedure for the Disciplinary Committee

The procedure for the Disciplinary Committee is set out in the General Optical Council (Disciplinary Committee Procedure) Order of Council 1969, SI 1969/1826. However, since the introduction of the Health and Social Security Act 1984 it has become apparent that the existing procedure is no longer adequate and the General Optical Council Disciplinary Committee (Procedure) Rules 1985 have appeared in draft form. The present section of text will outline the existing regulations and, where changes have been proposed, deal with the likely modifications to the regulations.

The preliminary proceedings are as follows.

1. A solicitor acting on behalf of the GOC, as soon as possible after referral of a disciplinary case to the Committee, serves the respondent with a notice of inquiry, sent by registered mail or by recorded delivery. This notice should state the charge or charges and specify the alleged convictions or other facts relating to each charge, together with the day, time and place of the Committee inquiry and should, in addition, contain a copy of the Opticians Act 1958 and a copy of SI 1969/1826 (or, when accepted, a copy of the new GOC Disciplinary Committee (Procedure) Rules 1985).
2. If there is a complainant then the solicitor should also send him/her a copy of the notice of inquiry and SI 1969/1826 (or the new GOC Disciplinary Committee (Procedure) Rules 1985).
3. An inquiry will not be held if a notice of inquiry has not been served in accordance with the above regulations.
4. An inquiry is not to be held within 28 days after the posting of the notice of inquiry, except with the agreement of the respondent.
5. The Chairman may, if he/she so wishes, or upon application by any party to the investigation, postpone the hearing. The Chairman may also refer a case to the Investigating Committee for further consideration as to whether an inquiry should be held. If any member of the Committee feels that there is a need to amend the notice of inquiry then, if necessary, an amended notice should be sent to the respondent and the inquiry postponed.
6. The solicitor to the GOC should notify, as soon as possible, all the parties concerned if the inquiry is to be postponed.
7. Upon application by any party to the inquiry, the solicitor to the GOC sends to that party a copy of any relevant document received by the Council from any party to the inquiry.

The next stage after the preliminary proceedings is the hearing itself and the procedure for this is as follows.

1. The charge or charges are read in the presence of the respondent and of the complainant, if one appears. If the respondent does not attend, however, the Committee may still continue and the charges are read out as if the respondent were present.

2. As soon as the charge or charges have been read out then the respondent, or his appointed agent, may object to all or part of the charge or charges made in point of law. Any other party may reply to any such objection. If the objection is upheld then no further proceedings will be taken on the section or sections to which the objection was raised.
3. The Chairman asks the respondent at this stage whether all or any of the alleged facts or convictions in the charge or charges are admitted.
4. The complainant, or his agent or the solicitor to the GOC then opens the case and may call witnesses and adduce evidence of any facts not admitted by the respondent which may be relevant. The respondent, or his appointed agent, may cross-examine any witness brought forward and the witness thereafter may be re-examined.
5. The respondent may then either:
   (a) submit that the evidence called at the hearing does not establish the charge alleged or does not merit erasure of the name from the register and the Committee may then consider any such submission; *or*
   (b) if no submission is made, or if the submission is not upheld by the Committee then the respondent or his agent may call witnesses and adduce evidence. Any such witness may be cross-examined by the complainant, his agent or the solicitor to the GOC and re-examined. The complainant, or his agent or the solicitor to the GOC may address the Committee on any point of law which the respondent or his agent may raise during his address following the examination of witnesses.
6. The Committee now deliberate and are asked to decide, in relation to each charge which remains outstanding, whether the facts alleged have been proved and, if so found, whether the facts substantiate the charge.
7. In the case of the Committee finding a charge proved, then the complainant, or his agent or the solicitor to the GOC, is required to adduce evidence as to the circumstances leading up to the charge.
8. The respondent may then address the Committee in mitigation and present any relevant evidence.
9. The Committee are now required to decide whether they can properly reach a decision to make no disciplinary order against the respondent, or to postpone judgement or to make a disciplinary order against the respondent.
10. If the Committee decide upon a postponement, they then specify either a period for which judgement is postponed or a further Committee meeting at which judgement will again be considered.

### Procedure upon postponement

1. The solicitor to the GOC sends to the respondent not less than six weeks before the day fixed for the resumption of proceedings a notice containing:
   (a) the day, time and place set for the resumption of the proceedings;
   (b) unless otherwise directed by the Chairman of the Committee, a letter inviting the respondent to furnish the names of character witnesses;

(c) an invitation to send any evidence relating to his conduct or any material facts which might have arisen since the original hearing. Any such information should reach the solicitor to the GOC no less than three weeks before the resumption of proceedings.

2. Any notice sent by the respondent after receipt of the above is passed on to the complainant for comment, and any such comment received by the solicitor to the GOC is supplied to the respondent.

3. At the resumed meeting, the solicitor to the GOC is invited to recall, for the information of the Committee, the position at which the case stands.

4. The Committee may now receive further oral or documentary evidence concerning the conduct of the respondent or any material facts which may have arisen since the original hearing.

5. The Committee then considers their decision as before. Relating to resumed proceedings, any new charge which may be alleged against the respondent may be heard provided that the correct procedure has been followed and a decision made concerning all the charges. There is no question of the validity of the Committee hearing even if the membership of the original inquiry and of the resumed proceedings differ. The Chairman may postpone the resumed proceedings, either upon application of involved parties or at his own discretion, in which case the procedure for resumption is repeated.

It is the function of the Disciplinary Committee to decide whether the provision of the Opticians Act 1958 or the rules of the Council have been contravened and to pass judgment accordingly. Any decisions made by the Disciplinary Committee are final, subject only to the right of appeal to the Judicial Committee of the Privy Council.

## Jurisdiction

Under the terms of ss. 11 and 13 of the Opticians Act 1958 the GOC have the power to erase from the register or list, the name of any optician or corporate body following a disciplinary hearing if:

1. A registered optician is convicted by any court in the UK of any criminal offence which renders him or her unfit to have his/her name in the register.

2. A registered optician is judged by the Disciplinary Committee to have been guilty of infamous conduct in any professional respect.

3. A body corporate is convicted of an offence under the Opticians Act 1958 or is found guilty of aiding, abetting, counselling or procuring the commission of or inciting another person to commit such an offence.

4. A body corporate no longer satisfies the criteria for enrolment as laid down in s. 4(2) of the Opticians Act 1958.

5. A registered optician or body corporate contravenes or fails to comply with rules made by the GOC under s. 25 of the Opticians Act 1958 so as to render him/her or it unsuitable for continued registration.

6. A registered optician or body corporate fails to ensure that optical appliances are fitted and supplied by or under the supervision of an appropriately qualified registered optician.

7. The original entry for enrolment of the register or list was fraudulently or incorrectly made.

The changes in the legislation for registered opticians brought about by the Health and Social Security Act 1984 have meant that the jurisdiction of the GOC has been modified and the new General Optical Council Disciplinary Committee (Procedure) Rules 1985 contain the following sections as an alternative to simple erasure:

1. An erasure order.
2. A suspension order. Under this new section the Committee specify the period, not exceeding 12 months, during which the respondent's registration or enrolment shall be suspended.
3. A penalty order. Any such order made under the new regulations will specify the sum (not exceeding £1000, payable to the GOC) and the period within which the sum specified is to be paid.
4. An erasure order or a suspension order together with a penalty order.

It can be seen that the new regulations are much more flexible than the old regulations. This means that it should be possible for the GOC to deal much more effectively with a much wider range of disciplinary matters.

### Disciplinary history of the GOC

Between the establishment of the Disciplinary Committee in 1960 and September 1982 there were 47 cases involving 101 charges against registered opticians or bodies corporate. On the basis of the hearings, 16 names were erased from the register or lists, and these may be broken down into:

9 cases of conviction by UK courts of a serious offence
4 cases of infamous conduct in a professional respect
3 cases of contravention of the GOC regulations made under s. 25 of the Opticians Act 1958, relating to publicity

The GOC has, in addition, made about 40 successful prosecutions against persons selling or supplying optical appliances contrary to the regulations under s. 21 of the Opticians Act 1958, limiting such acts to those qualified to be entered on the register or list.

# 7

# Professional ethics and disciplinary measures within the profession

## General ethics

At present there are two main sources of ethical and professional practice requirements for ophthalmic opticians/optometrists: the guidelines of the professional organisation, the British College of Ophthalmic Opticians (Optometrists); and the guidelines of the General Optical Council. Both organisations have facilities to take action in cases where the ethical codes are broken. The BCOO may take action against its own members and the GOC may take action against any registered ophthalmic optician/optometrist.

The BCOO have approved the following code of ethics.

'An ophthalmic optician [optometrist] shall always place the welfare of the patient before all other considerations and shall behave in a proper manner towards professional colleagues and shall not bring them or the profession into disrepute.'

The GOC, on the other hand, advise that for the protection of both individual patients and the public at large all registered opticians are expected to maintain the highest standards of experience, trading, performance and behaviour in all of their professional activities.

The BCOO has, in the few years since its formation, produced a set of guidelines for its members which will be updated as and when the Council of the College feel it necessary. These guidelines essentially set out the principles of proper professional attitude and conduct as interpreted by the elected Council of the College and cover four main areas:

'A. *Professional integrity*. It is the over-riding and continuing responsibility of all practitioners to place the welfare of their patients before all other considerations, and to apply to each patient the full extent of their knowledge and skill.

'B. *The practitioner/patient relationship.* The relationship between practitioners and patients is an individual relationship and depends on mutual trust: practitioners should do everything possible to promote and preserve their patients' confidence in them, and in the profession as a whole.

'C. *Advertising and publicity.* Practitioners should attract recommendation by the quality of the professional services which they provide. To seek to attract recommendation for any other reason is to mislead the public.

'D. *Premises and equipment.* The premises and equipment of practitioners should be such as to enable them properly to exercise their professional skills and to sustain a proper professional relationship with their patients, as set out in A and B, above.'

To back up these four criteria and the basic code of ethics and to help in the interpretation of specific areas, the BCOO gives a more extensive set of guidelines, reproduced below.

## Mode of practice

1. Ophthalmic opticians/optometrists are required to maintain a high standard of professional conduct and competence in the best interest of their patients, bearing in mind their scope of practice and the overall needs of the patient. Practitioners are reminded of their statutory obligations in this respect. They are advised, too, of their duty to protect themselves and their patients by carrying adequate professional indemnity cover.
2. Practitioners need to assure themselves of their competence to practise in specialised areas of ophthalmic optics such as contact lenses, orthoptics and industrial visual welfare, and are reminded of their responsibility for overall clinical care of their patients when visiting services are used.
3. Although no registered ophthalmic optician/optometrist is barred from undertaking contact lens fitting or orthoptic treatment, practitioners are advised that there is a risk to the public in such work particularly in the case of contact lenses. It is therefore important that such work not be undertaken without adequate training and experience. Suitable postqualification courses or supervised experience would be considered adequate training.
4. Practitioners should be prepared to recognise the limitations of their knowledge and skill, and, when they do so, to seek further advice.
5. Practitioners must scrupulously preserve the confidentiality of all information revealed by patients, and divulge such information only with the patient's consent or by order of a court of law.
6. The preservation of professional integrity remains the responsibility of individual practitioners however and wherever they practise. Practitioners should therefore always satisfy themselves that they have full freedom to do whatever in their professional opinion is necessary for each patient and that the circumstances and conditions of their practice in no way obstruct this freedom or interfere with the individual relationship between patient and practitioner.
7. Ophthalmic opticians/optometrists bear an individual professional responsibility for each of their patients and should practise in such a manner

that commercialism does not influence their judgement. To this end, ophthalmic opticians/optometrists should aim to work as individuals or within partnerships or group practices, or within the hospital eye service.

8. A partnership between an ophthalmic optician/optometrist and a person who is not an ophthalmic optician/optometrist carries certain risks relating to the welfare of ophthalmic patients, particularly on dissolution of the partnership. Ophthalmic opticians/optometrists are advised, therefore, to enter into partnership only with other ophthalmic opticians/optometrists. Where they are in partnership with persons who are not ophthalmic opticians/optometrists the partnership should not encompass the ophthalmic function.

9. An ophthalmic optician/optometrist who is professionally employed by or associated with any person, firm or company bears a responsibility for any action on the part of that person, firm or company which, had it been carried out by an ophthalmic optician/optometrist, could be considered unprofessional.

## Premises

1. The premises used by ophthalmic opticians/optometrists should reflect their purpose in providing a primary health care service. Their appearance should not seek to attract patients by the display of optical appliances and accessories visible to passers-by. Internally, the premises should be such as to ensure that patients will enjoy the privacy and comfort which they can reasonably expect to enjoy during any professional consultation.

2. The premises should comprise a fully enclosed unit with doors capable of being made secure, and be arranged so as to ensure that:
   (a) the examination and dispensing procedures are not disrupted by the general public or disturbed by external noise;
   (b) the confidentiality of patients' discussions on professional and personal matters are preserved;
   (c) patients' records are at all times secure and confidential.

## Equipment

Ophthalmic optical practices should be equipped and maintained so as to allow ophthalmic opticians/optometrists to investigate and prescribe in a manner appropriate to current standards and their own scope of practice.

## Continuing education

There is a duty upon all ophthalmic opticians/optometrists to maintain and expand their professional competence throughout their careers, since only in this way can they continue to offer the best possible service to the public. To this end they should attend refresher courses at regular intervals, actively support their local professional organisations, give attention to current literature and consider submitting themselves to higher examinations.

## Fees and charges

1. Where fees and charges are concerned, ophthalmic opticians/optometrists should take special care that patients know and understand the financial implications of professional services offered and of alternative methods of management, before they are asked to commit themselves to payment. To this end it is advisable to inform patients of the total cost to them in advance.
2. Ophthalmic opticians/optometrists should charge for their services on a professional system. This would comprise a fee for examination and advice, and dispensing fees appropriate to the work carried out to which is added the cost of any appliance or material provided.
3. Detailed statements of account should be rendered to patients, indicating that the charge includes a professional fee for consulting and/or dispensing services.

## Professional relationships

The preservation of the public's confidence in the profession as a whole depends in part upon the presentation to the public of a unified profession. The maintenance of proper relationships within the profession is therefore essential; this involves the careful application of the traditional professional courtesies and the avoidance of any action on the part of ophthalmic opticians/optometrists which could tend to be divisive.

## Relationships with other professions

1. Relationships with members of other professions should be conducted in a proper manner and in such a way that the individual responsibility of practitioners to their patients is not compromised in any way.
2. There are legal responsibilities upon all ophthalmic opticians/optometrists relating to the referral and reporting of cases to the medical profession; there are, however, additional moral and ethical responsibilities which must always be met. In particular, where an urgent case is referred to a hospital the patient's general medical practitioner must be informed. Unless members of the profession observe the traditional courtesies themselves, they cannot expect them to be reciprocated.

## Advertising

Practitioners should attract recommendation by their professional skill. Their patients should consult them for this reason alone and not because of the lure of advertisement or display on their premises, as this gives no indication of the standard or skill of service which will be provided.

## Use of titles and description of premises

If the public is to understand the professional nature of the services it receives from ophthalmic opticians/optometrists, it is essential that members of the profession and their premises are correctly described. The

College deprecates the use of any title or description other than 'ophthalmic optician' or 'optometrist'. The attention of Fellows and Members is drawn in this respect to the GOC's Notice N18.

## Practice succession

1. In all modes of practice, practitioners have a duty to ensure that when a particular association comes to an end or when a practice is sold or otherwise disposed of, the continuing welfare of their patients will be protected. Practitioners would be well advised to make sure that they will be able to meet this duty before entering any employment or association.
2. In the case of practice transfer, the name of the previous practitioner should not be retained for more than three years. This should apply whether the new owner of the practice is an individual, a partnership or a body corporate. In any event, the identity of the new owners must be clearly indicated from the commencement of the new ownership, whether or not the previous name is temporarily retained.

# Professional conduct

The GOC have guidelines regarding what they consider 'professional' conduct. These guidelines, which are to be revised, cover the following.

## Secrecy

It is considered the duty of ophthalmic opticians/optometrists to ensure that any information of a personal nature entrusted to their care will not be disclosed except when required by law.

## Discount arrangements

It is suggested that discount arrangements could mean that professional work is channelled to registered opticians or enrolled bodies corporate on financial grounds. Therefore no announcements should be made of discount arrangements and registered opticians and bodies corporate should not allow their name to appear in any lists of persons who give discounts.

## Premises

Professional activities of registered opticians and enrolled bodies corporate should be conducted in premises which ensure the maintenance of recognised professional standards.

## Association with lay business

It may be considered infamous conduct in a professional respect for a registered optician to remain in the employment of a lay employer (in any capacity) or for a registered optician to remain as a director, partner or member of any lay body corporate, partnership or unincorporated association when the business, to his knowledge, is carried on without regard to the principles of good professional conduct.

If a lay employer commits any act or omission which, if committed by a registered optician, would have amounted to infamous conduct in a professional respect or which would contravene any rules made under s. 25 of the Opticians Act 1958, the lay employer may be deemed to have acted without regard to the principles of good professional conduct.

### Refresher courses

No regulations or recommendations are made; simply a note to inform registered opticians of the improved opportunities to attend refresher courses.

### Fee splitting

The GOC recommend a registered optician should not share in the fees charged by another practitioner.

The FPCs of some regions have recently used the professional guidelines of the BCOO in conjunction with the GOC guidelines on general professional conduct to interpret some of the terms of service regulations. It is hoped that this will continue, as effective utilisation of the available recommendations should lead to a more ethically and professionally orientated ophthalmic service. At the present time failure to comply with the guidelines of the BCOO may lead to a disciplinary hearing and erasure of the name of the ophthalmic optician/optometrist from the College register. This does not mean that the practitioner will be prevented from practising, but use of the titles MBCO or FBCO may be suspended. Failure to comply with the GOC recommendations and guidelines may lead to erasure of the practitioner's name from the GOC register and therefore suspension from practice. It may be that at some future stage erasure from one list will mean automatic erasure from the other list, with the provision for appeal against such action; in this way the BCOO and the GOC could become more effective in their activities. It is unfortunate that the area of professional conduct is one which is open to varied interpretation. Despite the attempts of the BCOO to help in the interpretation of regulations, it is the GOC who have the more effective powers available and it is they who should perhaps be adopting a more strict approach to the matter of professional conduct, although recent amendments to the Opticians Act 1958 make such action more difficult.

# 8

# The European Economic Community and European legislation on ophthalmics

The professions of optometrists, ophthalmic opticians, ophthalmologists, dispensing opticians and optical mechanics are interwoven into a very complex structure throughout Europe. Each member country of the European Common Market has its own established hierarchy and its own protected titles and definitions. In terms of professional status and ability, the ophthalmic opticians/optometrists of the UK have always been ahead of the equivalent professional groups in other member countries. This situation has been slowly changing, with improvements in training and professional legislation throughout Europe and the recent legislation in the UK to allow unqualified sellers of spectacles to enter the market. Whilst the UK may still be ahead, the gap between the professions here and overseas is slowly shrinking.

The UK entered the EEC in 1972. Since then negotiations have been taking place between the various involved optical bodies and government representatives to produce legislation which will allow freedom to practise acceptable to all parties. The negotiations on behalf of the UK-based professions are carried out through the Joint Optical Consultative Committee on the Common Market. As the health services offered and the form of funding vary extensively throughout Europe, and as various member countries are awaiting new optical legislation, it is little wonder that progress is slow. Legislation has recently been proposed which will include optometry in a general directive but this has yet to be agreed.

It is important to study the differences between some of the European countries involved to understand the complexity of the situation. While there is still legislation pending it is possible only to outline the regulations.

## Belgium

Two rival organisations exist in Belgium, each sponsoring an optometry course. The older established and most supported organisation is l'Association Professionelle des Opticiens de Belgique; the more recently established is the Union Nationale des Optometristes et Opticiens de Belgique. Upon successful completion of one of the sponsored courses a candidate is offered a diploma, 'd'Opticien/Optometriste', signed by the Minister of Health. The

Diploma falls within the 'Cours Techniques Secondaires Supérieurs' classification and legally entitles the recipient to use the title 'opticien/optometriste'.

It was recently suggested that only one-third of the 2000–3000 opticien/optometristes who are legally eligible to refract actually do so. It also seems that less than 5 per cent of prescriptions issued originate from the opticien/optometristes. The major reason for this low percentage is the insistence of the health service agencies to pay for refractions and dispensing only when the prescription is issued by an ophthalmologist.

It seems a very strange situation when an eye examination and ophthalmic prescribing by opticien/optometristes have been virtually eliminated despite the existence of the legal right to refract. A royal decree of 1964 ensured the continuation of the privilege of objective and subjective refraction and contact lens fitting by the opticien/optometristes. A further development, by a decree in 1975, was the recognition of a two-tier profession by the introduction of a separate branch of dispensing opticians in addition to opticien/optometristes.

### Denmark

The optometric or ophthalmic profession in Denmark is relatively new. It was established as a profession separate from the crafts of instrument making and watch making by a government decree in 1954. Two organisations exist in Denmark to represent optometrists, and a third represents both ophthalmologists and optometrists. The groups are the Danish Society of Opticians, the Danish Society of Optometry and the Danish Contact Lens Association (the last representing the two professions).

Despite legislation and lengthy negotiations for some ten years there is as yet no statutory registration of refractionists in Denmark. Estimates put the number of practitioners examining eyes and fitting spectacles at 1000. This number is reduced if one considers objective refractive routines as well as subjective routines. There are restrictions applied which include no prescribing of prism, no prescribing of bifocals for children under 16 years of age and no refraction of children under 10 years of age. Despite this the Danish optometrists have established the right to receive payment for certain categories of service within the national health programme.

### Eire

The situation of ophthalmic optics in Eire is very similar to that in the UK. There is a two-tier system of ophthalmic and dispensing opticians who are regulated and registered by the Opticians Board established by the 1956 Opticians Act. In fact the Opticians Board has a function very similar to that of the GOC in the UK, being responsible for training standards, registration and the introduction of regulations. A form of health insurance exists under which free eye examinations are provided and a range of free spectacles are offered.

### France

The basic qualification for optometric registration in France at the present time is the 'Brevet de Technician Supérieur Opticien Lunetier'. Despite there being some 3000–4000 people holding this qualification, it has been estimated that 95 per cent of refractions are carried out by ophthalmologists. The legal attitude of the French courts to optometry was established by a ruling made in 1927, which stated that it was an illegal practice of medicine for an optician to attempt to direct a wearer of spectacles to use a particular prescription found by the optician.

Registration and licensing of optometrists was established in 1944. The original Bill laying down the terms for registration made it illegal to fit spectacles to children under the age of 16 years without a medical prescription, to use objective methods for determining the refraction and to use an ophthalmoscope. After the original Bill the restrictions hardened rather than eased. The year 1958 saw the introduction of a regulation making it compulsory for the majority of French citizens to take out health insurance which required an ophthalmologist's authorisation for reimbursement of refraction and spectacle charges. In 1962 a stipulation appeared in the *Journal Officiel de la Republique Francaise* stating

'The manipulation of instruments used in the determination of the ocular refraction' are 'medical acts . . . to be carried out only in accordance with article L.372 (1°) of the public health law.'

The restrictions have not stopped there, and the practice of orthoptics was denied by decree between 1965 and 1970. There is now, however, a move towards better training and qualification standards which may be the turning point for the French optometric profession. At present, courses in optometry are being offered at university level; with these going ahead, the profession will be put on a much better footing.

**Greece**

Greece is a relative newcomer to the Economic Community. It is probably unfortunate for the optometric profession that just prior to completion of membership formalities in 1979 the Greek government passed a Bill making it illegal for them to practise optometry. All eye examinations are carried out by ophthalmologists, and optometrists may only dispense.

The present situation is likely to remain for the foreseeable future although negotiations have taken place between members of the International Optometric and Optical League and representatives of the Greek Ministry of Health and Welfare. The talks covered the League's view on legislation, training, scope of practice and the benefits of optometric service. It is to be hoped that this initial contact will lead to a more tangible change in optometric legislation.

**Italy**

Registration in Italy as an 'ottico' (plural, 'ottici'; *ottica* = optics) is available via courses at eight institutions. A further advanced course offered by two of these Institutes leads to an optometric diploma. In addition to these existing courses, recent legislation through the Italian Chamber of Deputies laid the grounds for the establishment of three university schools of optometry. It is perhaps this which has led to a fairly strong position for optometry.

Optometry existed in Italy without statutory regulations until 1928. The enactment of law No. 1264 on 23 June 1927 regulating disciplines auxiliary to the health profession was followed by a royal decree issued on 31 May 1928 which defined the duties and privileges of ottici. Article 12 of the decree restricted the refracting rights of the ottici by requiring the authorisation of a medical physician when selling spectacles and lenses to the public. There were exceptions to the general rule, including simple myopia, presbyopia and duplication of spectacles, for all of which the ottici could prescribe.

The government definition of the scope of ottici stipulated the need to know objective and subjective refraction and visual analysis techniques as well as assessing eyewear in terms of the medical prescriptions available and the fitting of contact lenses upon medical authorisation. This broad definition gave considerable force to the proposal that the ottici were overqualified to act simply as 'dispensing opticians'.

It is estimated that there are about 6000 ottici and 1500 ophthalmologists in Italy. Although the tendency still seems to be for the ophthalmologists to carry out the eye examinations, the situation is rapidly changing. A 1975 estimate indicated that up to 40 per cent of all refractions were carried out by ottici.

The area of contact lenses is also of interest in Italy. A 1972 decree by the Ministry of Health prevented ophthalmologists from selling contact lenses. This has led to an estimated 90 per cent of all contact lens fitting being carried out by ottici.

## Luxembourg

The training to qualify as an independent optician in Luxembourg is seven and a half years: following a three-and-a-half-year apprenticeship with a practising optician and success at examination there follows a four-year period of practical education in opticians' workshops and theoretical education. On completion of the seven and a half years the student takes final exams to qualify as a master optician which gives one the right to practise as in independent optician and carry out examinations and supply spectacles.

## Netherlands

Optometrists in Holland enjoyed relative freedom as regards eye examination until the revision of the Medical Act in 1938. In this Act, however, a definition of ophthalmology made it clear that the optometrist would be allowed to carry out only subjective examination. The statute laid down that the use of trial lenses and a letter chart was not a medical act in law, but that examination of an organ and advice as to correction or alleviation of defects was. The Dutch profession accepted that this meant that retinoscopy and ophthalmoscopy were illegal acts.

A step forward from this position towards the recovery of professional status came with the establishment of formal registers of opticians as laid down by royal decree in 1966. This led to a commission report which included recommendations that a specific law be enacted to authorise optometrists to work in the areas of opticianry, optometry and contact lens fitting.

National elections in 1982 saw the rise of a new government and the present Minister of Health is planning to introduce legislation, called the Professions Individual Health Act, which will take up the recommendations of the commission. The result is likely to be a three-tier system providing for:

1. Opticians who dispense and carry out subjective examinations.
2. Opticians/optometrists who, in addition to category 1, will be allowed to carry out objective refractions.
3. Optometrists/contact lens specialists who will have the right also to carry out the fitting and supply of contact lenses.

## Federal Republic of Germany

Two basic divisions exist in the optometric profession in West Germany: the 'Augenoptikermeister' or master optometrist, and the 'Staatlich geprüfter Augenoptiker' or state examined optometrist. The Augenoptikermeister is the better placed of the two, having full privileges to own or manage a practice or business to sell and fit prescription eyewear, to undertake visual examinations for the purposes of prescribing spectacles, to fit and sell contact lenses, to fit and sell low vision aids, to receive reimbursement for services and materials from health insurance offices and to provide training for optical apprentices and assistants.

A series of court cases has established that under German legislation the acts of refraction, both subjective and objective, should not be considered medical acts. Other aspects of optometric practice such as orthoptics and tonometry are not undertaken except in co-operation with an ophthalmologist. There is no legislation to cover the referral of patients where ocular pathology is detected. A further legislative benefit to the optometric profession and, indirectly, to the public is the prohibition of the sale of over-the-counter reading spectacles by department stores.

The profession has suffered recently from other government legislation in which it was decided that the legal health system insurance cover extended to the supply of spectacles only once every three years unless there were significant changes in vision. This, combined with a government price freeze on optometric fees and prices of optical appliances, has seen the demise of many independent practitioners. Despite this, the number of refractions carried out by the Augenoptiker in 1982 was put at 28 per cent of the total.

The situation over all in Europe is, as initially stated, extremely complex. In many countries one finds practitioners carrying out the optometric function with apparent immunity despite the current legislation, and it is only when occasional problems arise that action is taken. The entry of the UK into the EEC caused an initial short-lived stir, and now it seems that there is little activity on all sides. The agreement to allow Portugal and Spain to enter the EEC is likely to further complicate the optometric picture, thereby forestalling again the need for any activity. As it stands at the moment the profession has to watch the European situation very carefully and be prepared to fight to prevent a further dilution of the optometric function in the UK and subsequent reduction in standards of eye care. With this complex situation it is inevitable that not all the information made available to the Government will be up to date, and it is disappointing to note that the Office of Fair Trading Report of 1982 carried several inaccuracies.

## 9
# Aspects of general law relating to ophthalmic practice

It is important for a practitioner to be aware of certain aspects of the general law which apply to everyday situations. Some of these aspects are associated with familiar daily routines such as contract law relating to a practitioner contract with the family practitioner committee (FPC). There are other areas, for example partnership and sale of goods, which it is important to understand as they again are likely to affect professional life. In this chapter some of the more commonly met legislation will be outlined. If ever a problem arises, however, it is important that the advice of a qualified solicitor is sought.

### Partnership law

The law on partnership is based on the Partnership Act 1890, with special provisions for limited partnership dealt with in the Limited Partnerships Act 1907. According to the 1890 Partnership Act,

'Partnership is the relation which subsists between persons carrying on a business in common with a view of profit.'

The rights and duties of the partners among themselves will vary in accordance with the partnership agreement, but there are a number of statutory requirements within the Partnership Act 1890 which will be presumed to apply wherever an agreement is lacking in detail. These requirements are:

1. Partners are each entitled to share equally in both the capital and the profits of the firm, but do not have any rights to payment for working on partnership business.
2. Disputes relating to the operation of the firm are settled by a majority decision, except in cases where unanimity is called for, such as the introduction of new partners or the change of business of the firm.
3. Unless specific arrangements are made for sleeping partners, every member of the partnership has the right to participate in the management of the firm.

4. Partners have the authority to inspect the books relating to the partnership business at any time, and books should be kept at the place of business of the partnership for this purpose.
5. Members of the partnership have a right to be indemnified by the firm for liabilities incurred in the course of executing the firm's business.

The Partnership Act 1890 laid down certain provisions covering the formation of a partnership:

1. No partnership may be formed consisting of more than 20 persons (except for banking where the permitted number is 10, according to the Companies Act 1948. Solicitors, accountants, auctioneers, estate agents and members of the stock exchange are also exempted under the Companies Act 1967 and the Board of Trade Regulations 1968).
2. If partners intend to carry on business under a name which is not the names of all the partners, such a name must be registered together with the names of the partners, and a certificate of registration obtained (Registration of Business Names Act 1916).
3. A partner cannot compete directly with the firm he belongs to, nor derive personal benefit from the firm's business, without the prior consent of the other partners.
4. Each partner in a firm is treated as an agent for the firm, and his fellow partners are legally liable upon contracts made or torts committed by a partner while acting on the firm's behalf.
5. Partners are jointly liable on the firm's contracts and jointly and severally liable for the firm's torts to the last penny of their personal fortune unless the partnership is a limited partnership formed and registered under the Limited Partnerships Act 1907. A limited partnership must still have at least one general partner whose liability is unlimited; if, however, a limited partner participates in the management of the firm then the limitation of liability is lost.

When forming a partnership it should be treated as a business arrangement and should therefore be put on a strictly business footing. Agreements should be drawn up by a solicitor, and, although the terms of any such agreement will vary considerably, the following items should be included.

1. The duration of the partnership. This may be for a fixed number of years or for an indefinite period.
2. Shares in capital and profits. The agreement should specify the share of the capital and the share of the profit to which each partner is entitled. Provision may be made for a gradual increase in share holding for a junior partner working his way into the firm.
3. Provision for retirement. An agreement should specify in detail the procedure for the retirement of partners and will usually give the continuing partners the right to acquire the outgoing partner's share on specified terms including the payment of a lump sum and/or an annuity to the outgoing partner. Such details should also apply in the case of the death of a partner.

4. Competition. A clause may be introduced to prevent a partner who leaves the firm from carrying on a business in competition with the partnership within a specified distance.
5. Expulsion. The agreement should specify the circumstances under which a partner may be expelled or forced to retire from the firm.
6. Arbitration. As no agreement covers all eventualities, however carefully it is planned, it is possible to maintain a clause which provides for arbitration by an independent body in cases of dispute within the partnership.

Any partnership, however formed, may be dissolved under the following circumstances.

1. By the expiry of the period of agreement.
2. By the completion of the particular undertaking for which the partnership was formed.
3. By the death or bankruptcy of any partner where no arrangements for this circumstance have been included in the partnership agreement.
4. By the mutual agreement of the partners.
5. By order of the court following an application made by any partner under the following circumstances:
   (a) where a partner is suffering from a mental disorder or is otherwise incapable of carrying out his obligations to the firm;
   (b) where an allegation is made that a partner's conduct is liable to prejudice the successful continuance of the business or that his behaviour is in breach of the partnership agreement, making continued co-operation almost impossible;
   (c) where a partnership in commercial practice cannot make a profit;
   (d) where the termination of a firm is seen to be a fair and equitable solution to the firm's problems.

## Corporations

Prior to 1844 most industrial and trading business was carried on either through partnerships or unincorporated associations. After that date, however, various Companies Acts were laid down culminating in the Companies Act 1948 and the Companies Act 1967. The result was that businesses were given the benefit of incorporation, particularly the benefit of limitation of liability of their members. Registration of a company is effected by depositing the following documents with the Registrar of Companies:

1. Memorandum of association. This is the company charter, defining its constitution and the scope of its power. If the company is limited by shares then the memorandum must state:
   (a) the name of the company with 'limited' as the last word in the name;
   (b) the country in which the registered office will be sited;
   (c) the objects of the company;
   (d) a declaration that the liability of the members of the company is limited;
   (e) the amount of share capital to be issued and the type of share.

2. Articles of association. These are regulations governing the internal management of the company. They define the duties of the directors and the mode or form in which the business will be carried out.

There are three types of registered company defined in terms of the level of liability:

1. A registered company limited by shares in which the liability of the members to pay the debts of the company is limited to the amount unpaid on their shares, if any.
2. A registered company limited by guarantee in which the liability of members to pay the debts of the company is limited to the amount guaranteed and payable only if the company is wound up.
3. An unlimited company in which the liability of the members to pay the debts of the company is unlimited.

Registered companies may also be divided into two classes based not on the limit of liability but according to the number of members, as follows:

1. Public companies. These have a minimum of seven members and have shares which are freely transferable on the share market.
2. Private companies. These have a minimum of two members and a maximum of 50 (not counting members who are past employees) and shares which are not freely transferable on the open market. The articles of association of such companies generally contain some provision for the sale of members' shares.

In law there are advantages and disadvantages to incorporation. The more important legal consequences of incorporation are:

1. The corporation or company can be sued in its own name and may be prosecuted for criminal offences; it may also sue under its own name.
2. Once incorporated the company forms a legal personality separate from the personalities of its members whom it can therefore sue and who can sue the company, and with whom the company can make contracts.
3. The corporation can, within the limits of its powers, trade like an ordinary individual.
4. The corporation or company can make contracts in its own name through human agents.
5. The corporation can own and dispose of property like any ordinary individual.

When a corporation has been created by law then it must act within the powers which have been granted; this is the so-called *ultra vires* doctrine. The powers of a corporation are defined in the memorandum of association of a registered company. Any contract made outside the powers of the company according to the *ultra vires* doctrine will be considered void.

Once formed, there are specific legal means for the termination of a company. The agreement may be terminated:

1. By the Registrar of Companies striking the company name from the register, having first satisfied himself that it is no longer trading.
2. By voluntary winding up after mutual agreement of the members of the company.

3. By compulsory winding up following an order of a court due to:
    (a) inability to pay debts;
    (b) failure to commence business within one year of formation;
    (c) failure to hold the statutory meeting or to file the statutory report or to maintain minimum numbers.

**Contracts**

A contract is a legally binding agreement, i.e. one which will be enforced by the courts. According to Sir William Anson, a contract may be defined as:

'A legally binding agreement made between two or more persons, by which rights are acquired by one or more to acts or forebearances on the part of the other or others.'

In practice, contracts form a basic part of the business and clinical activities of the practitioner. Certain essential factors are required for a simple contract to be considered valid in law. An agreement will be enforced, therefore, only when the following elements exist.

1. Offer and acceptance. There must be an offer made by one party and this offer must be accepted by the other party.
2. Intention. There must be an intention to create legal relations between the parties concerned.
3. Capacity of the parties. Each party involved must have the legal capacity to make the contract.
4. Consent must be genuine. A contract will not be considered valid if consent has been obtained by fraud or duress, for example.
5. Consideration must be present; i.e. some right, interest, profit or benefit.
6. Legality of objects. The objects and aims of the contract must be within the law.
7. Possibility of performance. The contract must be one which is capable of being performed.

All of the above elements are required to be present for a simple contract to be considered legally binding. If one or more is absent from the contract then one of the following may be considered.

1. Contract void. In this case it is destitute of legal effects; that is, it is not a contract and no legal rights may be conferred on the parties concerned.
2. Contract voidable. In this case the contract may be made void at the instance of one of the involved parties.
3. Contract unenforceable. Here the contract would be valid but is not enforceable because of:
    (a) the absence of evidence of the contract;
    (b) the absence of the legally required format.

The simple contract is not the only type of contract which exists in law, but it does tend to be the most important and by far the most common type. For information regarding other forms of contract, it is advisable to consult a solicitor.

## Law of tort

A branch of civil law which is of importance to the ophthalmic optician is the law of tort. This may be defined as:

A civil wrong for which the remedy is a common law action for unliquidated damages and which is not exclusively the breach of a contract or the breach of a trust and other merely equitable obligation.

As the definition states, tort is a civil law term; originating in France, it means simply 'a wrong'. It is used in English law to denote wrongs committed by one citizen against another serious enough to merit the award of compensation to the injured person but not serious enough to amount to a breach of criminal law.

Frequently contract law and law of tort overlap, although certain distinctions can be made. The following points are therefore of importance.

1. If the plaintiff cannot sue without proving the existence of a contract then the action is for breach of contract and not for tort.
2. In contract law the duties of the parties concerned are fixed, usually by the same parties, whereas in law of tort the duties are fixed by the law.
3. A person who is not a party to a contract cannot sue for breach of contract even though the breach may have caused that person damage. If, however, a defendant's action is also a breach of a legal duty then any person affected can sue in tort.

The most common form of present day action for tort is in the tort of negligence. To succeed in an action for negligence the plaintiff is required, for all practical purposes, to prove the following.

1. There exists a duty of care owed personally by the defendant to the plaintiff.
2. The duty of care has been broken.
3. Harm has been suffered as a result of the breach of duty.

Tort of negligence may then be defined as:

A breach by the defendant of a legal duty of care which is owed to the plaintiff among others and breach of which causes damage to the plaintiff.

To prove condition 1, above, requires that the defendant could reasonably have been expected to have seen that a person such as the plaintiff might be affected by his act or failure to act. This is not always easy to prove.

If the court agrees that a duty of care was owed then the plaintiff still has to prove that the duty was broken and that the behaviour of the defendant was sufficiently careless as to make it reasonably foreseeable that some injury to the plaintiff might result. Even if the defendant is able to show that he exercised care to the best of his ability, this may still not be considered adequate by the court. It seems that the courts tend to take the stand that a reasonable man takes extra precautions where the chances of an accident are greater or where the consequences of an accident may be more serious.

At this stage the plaintiff still has the task of proving that damage has resulted from the negligence committed and that this damage is a direct result of the incident.

It is possible for an act of negligence to lead to action both for breach of contract and for tort. For example, if *A* privately hires an optometrist, *O*, to carry out a sight test on a bedridden relative, *B*, and as a result of the examination, *O* negligently causes harm or fails to detect an abnormality in *B*, then two possible courses of action are available:

1. *A* may sue *O* for breach of a contractual duty of care.
2. *B* may sue *O* for the tort of negligence, i.e. the breach of the legal duty of care.

**Sale of Goods Act 1893**

With the recent legislative changes to 'open up competition' the business side of the ophthalmic optical/optometric profession has come to the fore. One very important area of the general law associated with this side of ophthalmic practice is the Sale of Goods Act 1893. The following conditions and warranties are implied in every contract for the sale of goods unless they are expressly excluded by the parties.

1. A condition that the seller has or will have a legal right to sell the goods at the time the transaction is to occur.
2. A condition in sales by sample that the bulk will correspond to the samples on which an order was based. In addition, the buyer should be given ample opportunity to compare sample and bulk, and the goods must be reasonably free of any defect not likely to be apparent on such examination.
3. A condition that in a sale where the seller provides goods as described by the buyer, the goods will correspond with the description.
4. A condition or warranty of quality or fitness for any purpose is implied only in the following circumstances:
   (a) where the seller is a specialist dealer in the goods sold and the purchaser makes it clear that he relies on the seller's judgement, a condition is implied that the goods shall be reasonably fit for the purpose intended if the purpose is specified;
   (b) where the seller is a dealer in the goods sold, there is an implicit condition that they shall be of merchandisable quality (i.e. of a generally acceptable quality);
   (c) an implied warranty or condition may be incorporated by the custom of a particular trade;
   (d) an express warranty or condition does not negate a condition or warranty implied by the Sale of Goods Act 1893 unless it is inconsistent therewith, in which case the express term excludes the implied term;
   (e) a warranty that the buyer shall enjoy quiet possession;
   (f) a warranty that the goods shall be free of any undisclosed charges or encumbrances in favour of any third party.

In the law of contract, where there is the possibility of misrepresentation the maxim has always been *caveat emptor* or 'let the buyer beware'. It is essential in the sale of goods that the buyer does everything possible to protect himself/herself. Protection should be in the form of obtaining as much information and as many assurances as possible from the seller.

**Trade Descriptions Act 1968**

A further Act of Parliament relating to the sale and supply of goods is the Trade Descriptions Act 1968. This is a criminal law Act which attempts to improve the accuracy of traders in describing the goods and services they offer to the public; it, too, is particularly relevant to the ophthalmic profession following the recent changes in the legislation. The relationships between the Trade Descriptions Act 1968, the Sale of Goods Act 1893, the Misrepresentation Act 1967 and contract law can be very complex. The main point, however, is that the consequence of breaking the Trade Descriptions Act is a criminal prosecution. This means that under this Act the outcome of any action is punishment and not just rescission of a contract or payment of damages.

The basic offences created under the Trade Descriptions Act 1968 are:

1. Applying a false trade description to goods.
2. Supplying goods to which a false trade description has been applied.

It is possible to adapt these general rules to cover services as well as goods.
There will be no offence committed if:

1. The inaccuracy is considered trifling.
2. The seller can show that the goods were believed to be as described and with reasonable care it was not possible to show that the goods differed from the description.
3. All reasonable precautions were taken and it can be shown that the misdescription was the result of a genuine mistake, the fault of someone else or due to a cause beyond the control of the defendant.

The Trade Descriptions Act 1968 details the points which may be found to constitute a trade description. These include:

1. The composition of the goods.
2. The method of manufacture.
3. The quantity.
4. The size.
5. The fitness for a specific purpose.
6. The performance in test and general use.
7. The date or place of manufacture.
8. The identity of the manufacturer.
9. The previous ownership of the goods.
10. Statements that the price has been reduced or is lower than the recommended price.

A prosecution is usually made following an inquiry by the local Weights and Measures or Trading Standards officials. Proceedings may be instituted on their own initiative or following a complaint from a member of the public. This legislation is also applicable to the unregistered seller of spectacles.

**Additional relevant law**

*Shops Act 1950; and Shops (Early Closing Days) Act 1965*

These Acts of Parliament relate to staff hours, trading days and times, and aspects of staff working conditions. The details of requirements under these

Acts will vary from area to area due to local council exemption orders and it is therefore advisable to seek local advice regarding details.

### Fire Precautions Act 1971; Fire Precautions (Non-Certificated Factory, Office, Shop and Railway Premises) Regulations 1976; Offices, Shops and Railway Premises Act 1963

These Acts and Regulations are concerned with the protection of people in the event of fire. There must be reasonable means of escape in the event of fire, there must be suitable equipment for fighting the type of fire likely to occur and the equipment should be maintained in efficient working order; also, all fire exits must be conspicuously marked. The regulations relating to fire are very important, and a fire certificate is required for premises other than those where 20 or less people are working at any one time, or where 10 or less persons are employed to work at any one time elsewhere than on the ground floor, or where there are other factory, office or shop premises in the same building but the sum total of employees is 20 or less. In most areas the local fire prevention officer is willing to help with advice and information and should be consulted if in doubt about requirements.

In addition to the above, the Offices, Shops and Railway Premises Act 1963 requires premises to be registered if there are any employees. It also lays down requirements relating to staff comfort and convenience, including ventilation and lighting, toilet facilities, rest rooms, drinking water and the maintenance of a minimum reasonable working temperature of 16°C.

### Health and Safety at Work etc. Act 1974

This Act applies to all persons at work, however small the business. It is designed to protect the people at work and the health and safety of the general public who may be affected by the work environment. According to the Act, it is the duty of every employer to ensure, as far as is reasonably practicable, the health and safety of employees. In addition to providing and maintaining a safe working environment the employer has to provide information, instruction, training and supervision to reasonably ensure the health and safety of employees; an adequate first aid kit also must be provided. Under the legislation, the employee has a duty to conform to statutory requirements, to take reasonable care to avoid injury and not to misuse or interfere with equipment provided. Where five or more employees are working, a written statement must be prepared outlining general policy with regard to health and safety at work and a safety officer should be appointed.

This chapter simply outlines some of the main points associated with the various Acts described. Should any problems arise, it is essential to seek qualified advice from a solicitor.

# 10

# Employer/employee legislation

## Contracts of employment

The Employment Protection (Consolidation) Act 1978 requires that all employers provide, within 13 weeks of the commencement of employment, written particulars of certain of the fundamental terms of the contract of employment. The following terms must be included in the written statement.

1. The name of the employer and of the employee.
2. The job title, which should include a short description of the scope of work intended.
3. The date of commencement of employment.
4. The scale of remuneration and the intervals of pay.
5. The normal hours of work (any expected overtime commitments should also be recorded).
6. Holiday entitlement and rates of holiday pay, including public holidays.
7. Particulars of any pension scheme or pension and whether the employee is contracted out of the state pension scheme. If no pension or scheme is available, this must be noted.
8. Terms and conditions relating to incapacity due to injury or sickness. If there are no such details then the contract need not say so.
9. The period of notice an employee is required to give and is entitled to receive.
10. Details of previous employment if counting towards the period of continuous employment.
11. Disciplinary rules and procedures.
12. Details of the person, by name or job description, to whom the employee can go in the case of any grievance, together with details of the grievance procedure.

Exemptions from the above requirements are an employee whose spouse is the employer.

## Rights of the employee on dismissal

There are three ways in which dismissal can occur, according to the Employment Protection (Consolidation) Act 1978:

1. The employer can terminate the employment either verbally or in writing.
2. A contract may have been for a fixed term and come to an end without being renewed.
3. The employer may be in breach of a fundamental term of the contract of employment, entitling the employee to leave without notice. (This particular case is called 'constructive dismissal').

If an employer dismisses or is found to have 'constructively dismissed' an employee, the dismissal may be considered unfair unless it was for one or more of the following permissible reasons.

1. Related to the capability or qualifications of the employee for the type of work for which he was employed.
2. Related to the employee's conduct.
3. A redundancy situation existed.
4. A statutory restriction was placed on the employer or employee such that continuation of the employment contravened the law.
5. Some other substantial reason.

The provisions for unfair dismissal do not apply in the following situations.

1. Where an employee has not completed 52 weeks of continuous reckonable service.
2. Where the employee is part-time, normally working less than 16 hours per week.
3. Where the employee has reached retirement age.
4. Where the employee is on a one-year fixed contract and has agreed in writing during that time to forgo any right to compensation at its expiry.
5. In certain lock-out or strike situations.
6. Where the total length of employment does not exceed two years and during that period there have been not more than a total of 20 employees, provided that employment commenced on or after 1 October 1980.
7. Where the employee is the employer's spouse.

In addition to the above general circumstances, there is a set procedure which must be followed in cases of dismissal to prevent the case being considered unfair by virtue of default in procedure. The guidelines are contained in a government-produced Code of Practice which is regularly updated. At present the following recommendations should be complied with.

1. All employees should receive copies of the employer's disciplinary procedure(s).
2. Employees should be entitled to answer any complaints against them and be accompanied at such a meeting by a colleague or union representative.
3. No employee should be automatically dismissed for a first offence unless it involves gross misconduct.
4. The case should be fully investigated before any action is taken and responsibility for action should not rest with the immediate superior but with a higher authority.
5. A full explanation of any penalty and its reasons should be given to an employee, together with notification of the right to appeal and the procedure to be followed.

6. Where disciplinary action other than dismissal is contemplated, this should be preceded by a formal warning in the case of minor offences and a written warning for serious offences.
7. A criminal offence committed outside of the employment should not be considered an automatic reason for dismissal.

The whole area of unfair dismissal is a complicated one and the above simply outlines some of the details. For further information it is advisable to consult a solicitor who has specialist knowledge of industrial law.

## Redundancy

Parliament first introduced the idea of redundancy payments as compensation for staff being made unemployed due to specific reasons. Basically, any employee is eligible for redundancy payment, with the following exceptions.

1. Where the emloyee has not completed at least two years of continuous service since the age of 18.
2. Where a man is 65 years or over or a woman is 60 years or over.
3. Where the employee is a part-time worker generally employed for less than 16 hours per week.
4. Under the conditions of certain fixed-term contracts.
5. The employee is the employer's spouse.
6. Where an employee refuses an offer of suitable alternative employment within four weeks of the redundancy date.

The term 'redundancy' is meant to cover termination of employment attributable wholly, or in the main, to:

1. An employer ceasing or intending to cease the business upon which the employee was working.
2. An employer ceasing or intending to cease the business at the place at which the employee was working.
3. Requirements of the business changing such that the particular kind of work of the employee is no longer needed or is needed less or is likely to be needed less.

If an employee is made redundant then the employer is liable to pay on the following scale based on the number of complete years of service up to a maximum of 20 years:

1. Aged 18 but under 22: entitled to ½ week's pay × number of completed years of service.
2. Aged 22 but under 41: entitled to 1 week's pay × number of completed years of service.
3. Aged 41–60 (women) or 41–65 (men): entitled to 1½ week's pay × number of completed years of service.

A week's pay is considered as subject to a maximum of £130.00.

The employer is not liable for the whole of this sum and may, under the terms of the Employment Protection (Consolidation) Act 1978, claim a rebate of 41 per cent of the payment from the Redundancy Fund using the relevant form obtained from the local Department of Employment Office.

### Equal Pay Act 1970

The Equal Pay Act 1970 (as amended by the Sex Discrimination Act 1975) and the Sex Discrimination Act 1975 were introduced in order to remove discrimination against women in employment. Both of these Acts are interlinked with article 119 of the Treaty of Rome and subsequent directives.

The Equal Pay Act is concerned with:

1. Instances where an employee of any age of one sex receives less favourable rates of pay than an employee of the opposite sex under a contract of employment with the same or an associated employer.
2. Instances where an employee of any age receives less favourable contractual terms than an employee of the opposite sex.

The provisos are that in both cases the work they are doing is:

1. The same.
2. Broadly similar such that any differences are not of practical importance.
3. Of equal value as determined by a 'job evaluation'.

### Sex Discrimination Act 1975

This Act complements the Equal Pay Act 1970. It established the Equal Opportunities Commission to investigate and eliminate wherever possible discrimination of all types in employment. Under the terms of the Sex Discrimination Act 1975, it is unlawful for an employer in Great Britain to discriminate against a man or a woman on the grounds of his or her sex or marital status. The legislation covers recruitment, terms and conditions of employment, training schemes, promotion, benefits and facilities. Only employers with five or more employees (whether full time or part time) are liable under the terms of the Sex Discrimination Act 1975.

### Employers' Liability (Compulsory Insurance) Act 1969

In order to protect employees this law requires that all employers insure against personal liability for personal injury to their employees. To comply with the Act employers must:

1. Take out an approved policy with an authorised insurer against liability for bodily injury or disease resulting from and during the course of employment.
2. Display a copy of the certificate of insurance in an easily accessible position where employees are able to view the certificate.

### Health and Safety at Work etc. Act 1974

The Health and Safety at Work etc. Act 1974 applies to all persons at work, including the self-employed but excluding domestic servants in private households; it is designed to protect people at work and the health and safety of the general public who may be affected by activities of those at work. The legislation requires that an employer ensures as much as possible the health and safety of his employees by:

1. Providing and maintaining machinery and systems of work which are safe and without risk to health.
2. Making arrangements to ensure the safety and health of employees when using, handling, storing and transporting articles and substances.
3. Providing instruction, information, training and supervision to ensure the safety and health of employees.
4. Providing and maintaining a safe workplace and safe access and exit from the place of work.
5. Providing and maintaining a safe a healthy working environment, with adequate facilities and arrangements for the welfare of employees at work.

All of the legal requirements of the Acts discussed above are more detailed than presented in this chapter. It is therefore important that, if any situation arises relating to employment, a suitably qualified solicitor be approached to provide expert advice.

# 11

# The law relating to the use of drugs

## Medicines Act 1968

In January 1978, the Government published the long-awaited statutory instruments bringing into force Part III of the Medicines Act 1968, and announced that the 'appointed day' would be 1 February 1978. Such was the extent of the change made in these orders that a further Order was made later, postponing certain of the provisions for six months to give the pharmaceutical industry and the profession of pharmacy sufficient time to come to terms with the new regulations concerning the sale and supply of some drugs.

Not least to be affected by the new regulations was the ophthalmic optician/optometrist, who now has the right to supply, as well as use, an even greater range of drugs than before. In order to fully understand the provisions relating to the use of drugs by ophthalmic opticians/optometrists, it is necessary first to summarise briefly the various parts of the Medicines Act 1968 and then look at the various Orders made under it which will affect ophthalmic opticians/optometrists.

The Medicines Act 1968, covering as it does such a wide range of activities concerned with the production and supply of medicines, is no mean document and is divided into eight parts, containing in all 136 sections and eight schedules. Schedules 5–8 list all the previous enactments to be repealed or amended with the coming into force of the main Act.

Part I of the Medicines Act 1968 deals with administration; s. 2 set up the Medicines Commission and Committees under it. The Medicines Commission consists of not less than eight members, representing the following 'activities' – medicine, veterinary medicine, pharmacy, pharmaceutical industry and chemistry.

The 45 sections of Part II deal with the licensing of the manufacture, import, export and wholesale of medicinal products. No person may manufacture or assemble or wholesale any product unless he has a license to do so. Such a 'blanket' law is, of course, subject to many exemptions. For example, it would be time consuming for a pharmacist to obtain a license every time he wished to make a particular prescription for a particular patient and so he is exempted from the necessity of obtaining a licence for manufacture under these conditions. There are further exemptions for doctors, dentists, veterinary practitioners, nurses and midwives. There are also exemptions for herbal remedies and transitional exemptions for products which were on the market on the appointed day.

The most important sections as far as the ophthalmic optician/optometrist is concerned are included in Part III, which deals with the sale or supply of medicinal products. In order to understand the various Orders introduced in February 1978 it is necessary to look at certain sections of this Part in detail.

Section 51 allows the Minister to set up a 'General Sale List' of drugs which can be reasonably sold without the supervision of a pharmacist. Section 53 allows for certain drugs to be sold by automatic machine (i.e. an automatic machine section to the General Sale List).

All drugs not on this list may be sold only by 'a person lawfully conducting a retail pharmacy business' or on premises registered as a pharmacy and under the supervision of a pharmacist (s. 52). This restriction used to be applied by including a substance in Part I of the Poisons List, when sale could be made only by an 'authorised seller of poisons' (note the change in title). Now, paradoxically, it is the non-inclusion of a substance in a list which brings this restriction into force. A very important rider which begins s. 52 (and other sections we shall be looking at) is 'subject to any exemption conferred by or under this part of the Act', since it allows certain substances to be sold other than at a pharmacy, even if they are not included on a General Sale List.

Sections 53 and 54 lay down the conditions under which General Sale List substances may be sold, and ss. 55–57 lay down broad exemptions from s. 52.

Further restrictions are imposed under s. 58, which allows for the setting up of another list of medicinal substances called the 'Prescription Only List'. Under subs. (2), medicines on the Prescription Only List can be supplied only in accordance with a prescription issued by an 'appropriate practitioner' (a term defined in subs. (1) as being doctors, dentists or veterinarians). The rest of s. 58 deals with exemptions from this restriction subject to conditions which may be defined in the relevant Orders.

The rest of Part III deals with other conditions concerning the sale or supply of medicinal substances and need not concern us here (especially s. 67, which deals with fines and imprisonment for contravening ss. 52 and 58).

Parts IV, V, VI, VII and VIII deal with pharmacies, containers, promotion of sales, official publications and miscellaneous provisions respectively.

Nowhere in the Act are specific medicinal substances listed. The inclusion of substances in the General Sale List or in the Precription Only List is the subject of the various Orders brought into effect on 1 February 1978. Principal among these are the General Sale List and the Presciption Only List.

## General Sale List

The General Sale List is a list of human and veterinary drugs, and contains the common (and some not so common) medicinal substances which can be sold other than at a pharmacy. Provided that s. 53 is complied with, an ophthalmic optician may sell any substance on the General Sale List.

Schedule 6 of the Order (SI 1977/2129), however, lists medicinal products which are not on the General Sale List and includes products marketed as eye drops or eye ointments. Thus all eye drops, whether for human or for animal use, are not on general sale even though the active principle is included in the list.

### Prescription Only List

It will surprise ophthalmic opticians to find that many of the drugs commonly in use by them are included in Sch. 1 of the Prescription Only List. Even though the schedule exempts many of these drugs from the class of prescription only when they are applied externally, local ophthalmic use is often excluded from the exemption. For example, atropine is prescription only unless applied externally by a route other than to the eye.

It can be seen that eye drops and eye ointment have been singled out for special attention both in their exclusion from the General Sale List and in the external application exemption from the Prescription Only List.

Schedule 4 is a list of exemptions from s. 58(2) – the section by which a prescription is required before drugs on the list can be supplied. Paragraph 5(3) allows pharmacists to supply certain specified eye drops or ointments subject to the presentation of an order signed by a registered ophthalmic optician. Paragraph 6 allows ophthalmic opticians to supply the same drugs in the course of their professional practice or in an emergency. The drugs covered by this exemption will be found in Appendix 2. Interestingly enough this schedule only gives exemption from s. 58 – it does not give exemption from s. 52 (supply only by a pharmacist). The exemption from this latter section is given in another completely separate Order – the Medicines (Pharmacy and General Sale – Exemption) Order 1977 – which exempts ophthalmic opticians/optometrists from the requirements of s. 52 for the same drugs in the schedule. This Order also provides a general, transitional exemption from s. 52 for products which could have lawfully been supplied before the appointed day, this exemption to last for two years.

One further Order, the Medicines (Sale or Supply) (Miscellaneous Provisions) Regulations 1977, SI 1977/2132, allows the ophthalmic optician/optometrist to obtain and use a further range of drugs. The particular regulation relates to wholesale dealing, which is defined in the Medicines Act 1968 as being supply to a person for retail sale, or for administering to a human being in the course of a business carried on by him. Since this Order does not give exemption from s. 52, only the latter purpose is catered for; i.e. ophthalmic opticians/optometrists may use these drugs in their practice but must not supply them to their patients. Most of the drugs in this Order are the local anaesthetics which should never be given to patients in any case.

One point of caution should be noted concerning the use of ecothiopate. This drug is supplied by the manufacturer as a dry powder and a sterile vehicle, each in a separate container, which are intended to be mixed prior to supply to the patient. Apart from the practical difficulties involved in aseptic preparation, it could be construed that mixing the powder with the vehicle constitutes assembling a medicinal product which is covered by Part II of the Medicines Act 1968. Pharmacists have a general exemption from this part of the Act when they are supplying individual patients; ophthalmic opticians/optometrists do not. If it is intended, therefore, to supply a patient with ecothiopate, it would be desirable to do this by way of a signed order to the pharmacist and not rely on keeping a stock of ready-made solution which is stable for only about one month under ideal conditions.

Although the Medicines Act 1968 is wide ranging in its effect, it is not the only Act which affects the sale and supply of drugs. So-called 'controlled drugs' are covered by the Misuse of Drugs Act 1971. All standard eye preparations of cocaine come under this Act and hence they cannot be used by the ophthalmic optician/optometrist.

In conclusions, it can be seen that the effect of the legislation is to increase the range of drugs which the ophthalmic optician/optometrist may use and supply. Apart from an emergency, the use or supply of drugs must be in line with the practice of the profession of ophthalmic optics as defined in the Opticians Act 1958 or laid down by the GOC. Nothing in the Medicines Act 1968 has changed the restrictions concerning treatment of adverse ocular conditions.

## Prescription writing

In the normal course of practice two situations may arise concerning the supply of drugs for use in the practice, in which case two courses are open. In the first situation, either the practitioner may write out a signed order or, in the case of a 'poison' (as defined in the Medicines Act) which is still available for use in the practice, he may sign the poisons register. The format for a signed order for physostigmine is:

| | |
|---|---|
| Name of practitioner, qualifications | Address of practitioner |
| Ophthalmic optician/optometrist | Date |
| Please supply, for use in my practice, | |
| X single dose units (minims)  Physostigmine salicylate BP 0.25% | |
| Signature of practitioner | |

The other situation which may arise concerning the supply of drugs is the use of a prescription to supply a substance such as atropine for instillation by the patient at home prior to his appointment for visual examination. In this second situation the format for the signed order for supply is:

| | |
|---|---|
| Name of practitioner, qualifications | Address of practitioner |
| Ophthalmic optician/optometrist | Date |
| Name of patient (and age if under 14 years) | |
| Address of patient | |
| Name and formula of preparation and strength | |
| Quantity to be supplied | |
| Labelling instructions | |
| Signature of practitioner | |

# 12

# Industrial eye protection

### Protection of Eyes Regulations 1974

Industrial eye protection plays an increasingly large part in modern ophthalmic practice. The Regulations now in force were drawn up in 1974 to replace s. 49 of the Factories Act 1937. The Protection of Eyes Regulations, SI 1974/1681, officially came into force on 10 April 1975. They cover some 35 processes for which approved eye protection is required and an additional five situations where persons may be at risk even when not specifically engaged in the particular process. Although this is the major source of information on eye protection, additional legal requirements may be necessary under the terms of the Factories Act 1961, the Protection of Eyes (Amendment) Regulations 1976 (SI 1976/303) and also the Health and Safety at Work etc. Act 1974.

The early Regulations required that suitable goggles for the particular task be provided. The exact definition of suitable goggles, however, was not given and therefore the legislation was of limited use. Additional specified eye protection requirements for specific purposes came within the scope of five statutory instruments and three British Standards covering a wide range of industrial work: SIs 1922/731, 1953/1464, 1960/1932, 1961/1580 and 1962/1667, and BSs 679, 1542 and 1729.

New legislation obviously was required to bring all of these separate aspects under one umbrella. What the Protection of Eyes Regulations 1974 in fact did was to require the provision of eye protectors for a much greater number of industrial jobs and processes. They also regulate standards for the eye protectors: it became necessary for them to conform to a specific certificate of approval. The certificates are of two types:

1. Certificate No. 1 (HMSO publication F 2475). This is subdivided into three schedules:
   Schedule 1 – specifying that eye protectors, shields and fixed shields should conform to British Standards BS 2092, BS 1542 and BS 679;
   Schedule 2 – specifying the marking which may be used by manufacturers;
   Schedule 3 – specifying the particular details which must accompany eye protectors.

2. Certificate No. 2 (HMSO publication F 2489). This relates to protection from easing sources, and also is subdivided into three schedules:
Schedule 1 – specifying the construction requirements (there is not as yet a relevant BS available);
Schedule 2 – specifying the marking which the manufacturer may use;
Schedule 3 – specifying the particular information which must accompany eye protectors.

In addition, the new Regulations laid down the responsibilities of employees with regard to the provision and wearing of eye protectors.

The Protection of Eyes Regulations 1974 requires the employer to provide safety eyewear for every person employed in any of a series of specified processes. The eyewear falls into three categories, listed below.

### Eye protectors

Eye protectors must be provided for use by persons employed in the following specified processes.

1. The blasting or erosion of concrete by means of shot or other abrasive materials propelled by compressed air.
2. The cleaning of buildings or structures by means of shot or other abrasive materials propelled by compressed air.
3. Cleaning by means of high-pressure water jets.
4. The striking of masonry nails by means of a hammer or other hand tool or by means of a power-driven portable tool.
5. Any work carried out with a hand-held cartridge-operated tool, including the operation of loading and unloading live cartridges into such a tool, and the handling of such a tool for the purpose of maintenance report or examination when the tool is loaded with a live cartridge.
6. The chipping of metal, and the chipping, knocking out, cutting out or cutting off of cold rivets, bolts, nuts, lugs, pins, collars or similar articles from any structure or plant, or from part of any structure or plant, by means of a hammer, chisel, punch or similar hand tool, or by means of a power-driven portable tool.
7. The chipping or scurfing of paint, scale, slag, rust or other corrosion from the surface of metal and other hard materials by means of a hand tool or by means of a power-driven portable tool or by applying articles of metal or such materials to a power-driven tool.
8. The use of a high-speed metal-cutting saw or an abrasive cutting-off wheel or disc, which in either case is power driven.
9. The pouring or skimming of molten metal in foundries.
10. Work at a molten salt surface if exposed.
11. The operation, maintenance, dismantling or demolition of plant or any part of plant, being plant or part of plant which contains or has contained acids, alkalis, dangerous corrosive substances, whether liquid or solid, or other substances which are similarly injurious to the eyes, and which has not been so prepared (by isolation, reduction or pressure, emptying or otherwise), treated or designed and constructed as to prevent any reasonably foreseeable risk of injury to the eyes of any person engaged in any such work from any of the said contents.

12. The handling in open vessels or manipulation of acids, alkalis, dangerous corrosive materials, whether liquid or solid, and other substances which are similarly injurious to the eyes, where in any of the foregoing cases there is a reasonably foreseeable risk of injury to the eyes of any person engaged in any such work from drops splashed or particles thrown off.

13. The driving in or on of bolts, pins, collars or similar articles to any structure or plant or to part of any structure or plant by means of a hammer, chisel, punch or similar hand tool, or by means of a power-driven portable tool, where in any of the foregoing cases there is a reasonably foreseeable risk of injury to the eyes of any person engaged in the work from particles or fragments thrown off.

14. Injection by pressure of liquids or solutions into buildings or structures or parts thereof where in the course of any such work there is a reasonably foreseeable risk of injury to the eyes of any person engaged in the work from any such liquids or solutions.

15. The breaking up of metal by means of a hammer, whether power driven or not, or by means of a tup, where in either of the foregoing cases there is a reasonably foreseeable risk of injury to the eyes of any person engaged in the work from particles or fragments thrown off.

16. The breaking, cutting, cutting into, dressing, carving or drilling by means of a power-driven portable tool, or by means of a hammer, chisel, pick or similar hand tool, other than a trowel, of any of the following:
    (a) glass, hard plastics, concrete, fired clay, plaster, slag or stone (whether natural or artificial);
    (b) materials similar to any of the foregoing;
    (c) articles consisting wholly of partly of any of the foregoing;
    (d) stonework, brickwork or blockwork;
    (e) bricks, tiles or blocks (except blocks made of wood), where in any of the foregoing cases there is a reasonably foreseeable risk of injury to the eyes of any prson engaged in the work from particles or fragments thrown off.

17. The use of compressed air for removing swarf, dust, dirt or other particles, where in the course of any such work there is a reasonably foreseeable risk of injury to the eyes of any person engaged in the work from particles or fragments thrown off.

18. Work at a furnace containing molten metal, and the pouring or skimming of molten metal in places other than foundries, where there is a reasonably foreseeable risk of injury to the eyes of any person engaged in any such work from molten metal.

19. Processes in foundries where there is a reasonably foreseeable risk of injury to the eyes of any person engaged in any such work from hot sand thrown off.

20. Work in the manufacture of wire rope where there is a reasonably foreseeable risk of injury to the eyes of any person engaged in the work from particles or fragments thrown off or from flying ends of wire.

21. The operation of coiling wire, and operations connected therewith, where there is a reasonably foreseeable risk of injury to the eyes of any person engaged in any such work from particles or fragments thrown off or from flying ends of wire.

22. The cutting of wire or metal strapping under tension, where there is a reasonably foreseeable risk of injury to the eyes of any person engaged in any such work from flying ends of wire or flying ends of metal strapping.
23. Work in the manufacture of glass and in the processing of glass and the handling of cullet, where in any of the foregoing cases there is a reasonably foreseeable risk of injury to the eyes of any person engaged in the work for particles or fragments thrown off.

### A shield or fixed shields

A shield or sufficient number of fixed shields must be supplied for the use of persons employed in any process involving the use of an exposed electric arc or an exposed stream of arc plasma.

### Eye protectors or a shield or fixed shields

Eye protectors or a shield or a sufficient number of fixed shields must be provided for the following processes.

1. The welding of metals by means of apparatus to which oxygen or any flammable gas or vapour is supplied under pressure.
2. The hot fettling of steel castings by means of a flux-injected burner or air carbon torch, and the deseaming of metal.
3. The cutting, boring, cleaning, surface conditioning or spraying of material by means of apparatus (not being apparatus mechanically driven by compressed air) to which air, oxygen or any flammable gas or vapour is supplied under pressure, excluding any such process elsewhere specified, where in any of the foregoing cases there is a reasonably foreseeable risk of injury to the eyes of any person engaged in the work from particles or fragments thrown off or from intense light or other radiation.
4. Any process involving the use of an instrument which produces light amplification by the stimulation emission of radiation, being a process in which there is a reasonably foreseeable risk of injury to the eyes of any person engaged in the process from radiation.
5. Truing or dressing of an abrasive wheel where in either of the foregoing cases there is a reasonably foreseeable risk of injury to the eyes of any person engaged in the work from particles or fragments thrown off.
6. Work with drop hammers, power hammers, horizontal forging machines and forging presses, other than hydraulic presses, used in any case for the manufacture of forgings.
7. The dry grinding of materials or articles by applying them by hand to a wheel, disc or band which in any case is power driven or by means of a power-driven portable tool, where in any of the foregoing cases there is a reasonably foreseeable risk of injury to the eyes of any person engaged in the work from particles or fragments thrown off.

The employer must replace any eye protector if it is lost or destroyed or is so defective as to be unsuitable for the purpose for which it was provided.

The employee must use any eye protector or shield provided at all times when working on any of the specified processes. It is also the responsibility of the employee to take reasonable care of the eye protectors or shields and to report any loss, destruction or defect in the eye protector to the employer or his agent.

A registered optician undertaking the supply of eye protectors to prescription is held fully responsible for the protector supplied. The visual professional and moral obligations apply but there are additional legal obligations which do not apply to the 'normal' refractive non-eye-protector prescription. Regulation 9 states:

'Eye protectors and shields provided in pursuance of these regulations shall

'a. be suitable for the person for whose use they are provided

'b. be made in conformity with an approved specification for eye protection or shields, as the case may be, being an approved specification for eye protectors or shields which are appropriate to the specified process in which the said person is employed or from the carrying on of which there is a reasonably foreseeable risk of injury to the eyes of the said person as the case may be

'c. be marked in such a manner and accompanied by such particulars as may be approved in order to indicate the purpose or purposes for which the eye protectors or shield were designed.'

## British Standards for eye protectors

Any appliance supplied for industrial protection must, in addition to the above, conform with the requirements laid down in BS 2092:1967. In order to ensure that the appliance is of the approved nature, the British Standards Institute licenses various prescription houses to apply the Kitemark to their products. It may, however, be necessary for certain industrial tasks to have special protectors which fall outside the scope of the Kitemarked protectors.

The initial industrial eye protectors British Standard was issued in 1954 and revised in 1962. BS 2092:1967 was a further revision to include eye protectors for use in the presence of hazards from high-speed flying particles or from flying molten metal or hot solids. If protectors are issued against harmful radiation, then, in addition to the general requirements, the specifications of several other British Standards should be met. For example:

BS 679 – filters for use during welding and similar industrial operations.
BS 2794 – Filters for protection against intense sunglare (for general and industrial use).

BS 2092 Specification for industrial eye protectors when revised laid down specifications for all types of eye protection against industrial hazards from:

1. Impact from high-speed flying particles.
2. Molten metal.
3. Dust.
4. Gas.
5. Chemical splashes.
6. Any combination of 1–5.

It applies not only to spectacles and goggles but also to eye screens and face screens (alternatively called visors and one-piece eye protectors).

The specifications cover the construction of eye protectors, the lenses used, the performance required and the test schedule which must be passed for devices to comply with the Standard. Goods which comply with these specifications are marked by the British Standards Institution registered trademark – the Kitemark; when applied to a product, it indicates to the purchaser that the item conforms with the relevant British Standard. To earn the Kitemark the article has to be manufactured under a strict scheme of supervision and control as laid down by the British Standard Institution. The actual markings for different industrial requirements are available from BS 2092:1967, but in general will consist of BS 2092 and the manufacturer's mark or license number.

According to BS 2092, lenses used in protective eyewear should comply with the following requirements.

1. They will transmit not less than 80 per cent of the energy within the visible spectrum unless they are in the impact-resisting group and are double-layered, in which case the transmission will not be less than 70 per cent (this is an interim figure and will be raised as other materials become available). These limits do not apply if filters to the relevant British Standards are incorporated to provide protection against radiation.
2. They will be free to within 3 mm (⅛ in) of the edge from inherent defects such as bubbles, grains and clouding, and from surface defects such as holes, scratches, cracks, waves and dull spots which can be observed by inspection by the naked eye (or with spectacles, if necessary) under conditions of adequate illumination against a suitable background. If a one-piece eye protector is moulded from a single piece of material, any distortion greater than that specified in requirement 5, below, will be outside the limits of the field of vision given in BS 2092 (paragraph 4.2).
3. In the case of individual lenses for industrial spectacles or industrial goggles having separate eye pieces, each lens must comply with the limitations of prismatic effect given in requirement 5, below.
4. For eye protectors incorporating a one-piece window or a face screen, the limitation of prismatic effect (requirement 5) applies to two circles each 52 mm in diameter. These two circles are spaced symmetrically about the vertical centre line of the eye protector and the distance between the centre of the circles is 62 mm, measured in the horizontal front plane of the eye protector as worn.
5. In eye protectors having separate eyepieces, the prismatic effect may not exceed 0.15 prism dioptres at any point on the lens when tested in accordance with Appendix M of BS 2092:1967. In one-piece eye protectors and face screens, the prismatic effect may not exceed 0.15 dioptres within the areas defined in requirement 4, when tested in accordance with Appendix M of BS 2092:1967.
6. Industrial spectacles with lenses to prescription must comply with the requirements of BS 2738, 'Spectacles Lenses'.

The tests as laid down by BS 2092 for suitability of protectors are as follows.

### Robustness of construction

All eye protectors must be designed and constructed to withstand a test for general strength of construction consisting of the impact of a 0.65 mm (¼ in) steel ball travelling at a velocity of 12.2 m/s (40 ft/s). The test is applied in accordance with Appendix B of BS 2092:1967. When so tested the eye protector must not show:

1. Lens fracture. A lens is considered to have fractured when it cracks through its entire thickness into two or more separated pieces or when more than 30 mg of the lens material becomes detached from the surface remote from that area receiving the test blow.
2. Lens deformation. A lens is considered to have deformed when a mark appears on the white paper appropriate to the striking face of the ball.
3. Lens housing or frame failure. A lens housing or frame is considered to have failed if it is fractured, if its parts separate or if it allows a lens to be knocked from its housing.

### Stability at elevated temperature

Assembled eye protectors must be stable at elevated temperatures, and when tested in accordance with the methods given in Appendix J of BS 2092:1967 must show no apparent physical distortion. On completion of the test, their robustness must not have fallen below that required as given above nor shall their optical qualities have deteriorated beyond the limits imposed by paragraph 4.3 of BS 2092:1967.

### Protection against impact

Eye protectors intended to provide protection against the impact of flying particles must be designed and constructed to withstand an impact test consisting of the impact on the lenses of a 0.65 mm (¼ in) steel ball travelling at a velocity of 119 m/s (390 ft/s) for Grade 1 or at 45.7 m/s (150 ft/s) for Grade 2.

Except where double lenses are used, the lenses of eye protectors giving protection against the hazard of high-speed (119 m/s (390 ft/s)) impact must, in the present state of development in this field, be made of plastics materials which by their nature are liable to scratch more easily, particularly in atmospheres laden with hard dusts, than are the more abrasion-resistant plastics capable of resisting only lower impact speeds. For this reason a lower grade of impact resistance is also specified (45.7 m/s (150 ft/s)) which, if chosen, can be achieved in eye protectors which are scratch resistant.

Investigation is taking place into the possibility of specifying the anti-abrasion qualities of eye protectors. The test will be applied in accordance with Appendix B of BS 2092:1967. When so tested the eye protector may not show:

1. Lens fracture. A lens is considered to have fractured when it cracks through its thickness or when one or more particles becomes detached from the surface remote from that receiving the test impact.
2. Lens deformation. A lens is considered to have deformed when a mark appears on the white paper appropriate to the striking face of the ball.

**TABLE 12.1. Quick reference chart relating requirements of the Protection of Eyes Regulations, SI 1974/1681, to the relevant British Standards**

| Sch. | Part | Process | Relevant clauses | BS applicable |
|------|------|---------|------------------|---------------|
| 1 | I | 1–8, 19–22 | Eye protectors clause 5(1)(a) | BS 2092 |
| | | 6–7 | Clause 5(2) requires fixed shield (not approved) to be used. Construction to meet function described in clause 10(c) | BS 2092 |
| | | 9, 10, 18 & 23 | These processes may also require BS 1542 or 679 or tinted lenses conforming to at least GP standard of BS 2092 | BS 2092 |
| 1 | II | 24 | Clause 5(1)(b) approved shield or fixed shields. Approval basically relates to clause 10(b) where the transparent section would need to comply with BS 679 | BS 1542 or 679 |
| 1 | III | 25–27 | Clause 5(1)(c) approved eye protectors, or approved shield or approved fixed shields. 'Approved fixed shields' as described above | BS 1542 or 679 |
| | | 28 | No BS applicable. See details of Certificate of Approval No. 2. For further information consult BS 4803 and ISO/DIS 6161 | |
| 1 | IV | 29, 31–34 | Clause 5(1)(c) approved eye protectors or approved shields | BS 2092 |
| | | 32 | Clause 5(2) fixed shields (not approved) to be used | |
| | | 30 & 35 | These processes may also require BS 1524 or 679 eye protection used in combination with BS 2092 or tinted lenses conforming at least to GP standard of BS 2092 | BS 2092 or 1542 or 679 |
| 2 | | 1, 2 & 4 | Clause 6(b) fixed shields (not approved) to be used, constructed to meet function as described in clause 10(c) | |
| | | 3 | Clause 6(a) eye protectors, or a shield or fixed shields provided by the employer of the employees at risk. | |
| | | 5 | Lasing devices – clause 6(b) applicable – as described above. If a transparent viewing window is incorporated into a fixed shield the requirement of clause 10(b) could only be met by fulfilling the specifications of Certificate of Approval No. 2 | |

Reproduced, with permission, from Roussell (1979)

3. Lens housing or frame failure. A lens housing or frame is considered to have failed if it is fractured, if its parts separate or if it allows a lens to be knocked from its housing.

Additional tests are carried out for specialised situations of use.

It is essential that the right grade of eye protector be provided for the process being undertaken, and this decision is a matter for the employer advised by the Chief Inspector of Factories. At present, prescription lenses can be supplied only to the general purpose grade of BS 2092. If the process requires a protector with a higher impact resistance and the patient is ametropic, there is no alternative to the wearing of eye protectors over spectacles (or contact lenses).

Table 12.1 (from Rousell, 1979) indicates the clauses and British Standards relating to the specified processes discussed in this chapter. Table 12.2 (also from Rousell, 1979) shows the range of eye protection available at the present time. These two in combination should provide a useful basis for assessing the requirements within a particular working environment.

**TABLE 12.2. Types of eye protectors covered by British Standards 2092 and 1542**

| Type | Spectacle | Cup goggles | Box goggles | Face screen |
|------|-----------|-------------|-------------|-------------|
| General purpose (GP) | + | + | + | + |
| Impact grade 2 (I2) | + | Pos | + | + |
| Impact grade 1 (I1) | NA | Pos | + | + |
| Molten metal (MM) | NA | + | + | + |
| Chemical splash (CS) | NA | NA | NA | + |
| Chemical droplet (CD) | NA | Pos | + | NA |
| Dust (D) | NA | + | + | NA |
| Gas (G) | NA | NA | + | NA |
| Impact plus MM | NA | Pos | + | + |
| Impact plus CS | NA | NA | NA | + |
| Impact plus CD | NA | Pos | + | NA |
| Impact plus D | NA | Pos | + | NA |
| Impact plus G | NA | Pos | Pos | NA |

NA, not applicable; Pos, possibly obtainable; +, definitely available.
Reproduced, with permission, from Roussel (1979)

As the general purpose protectors are not suitable for all types of environmental hazards, and in any case where doubt exists as to their suitability, then the person supplying the protectors should contact the local factory inspector for guidance. This is a very important aspect for the ophthalmic optician/optometrist as it is he or she who will take the ultimate responsibility following supply.

If at any time a safety spectacle needs repair either to the frame or to the lens, complete replacement is required for the protector to still comply with the Protection of Eyes Regulations 1974. Repairs or reglazes nullify the Kitemark guarantee and may lead to difficulties if at some future date the spectacles are involved in an accident claim, so always replace damaged safety spectacles no matter how small the fault.

# 13
# Standards of vision

It is often found that in practice patients ask the standards of vision required for various occupations. There is some difficulty in obtaining the information *en masse* and as a guide some of the more commonly requested requirements are therefore laid out below.

## Motor vehicle driving licence

Applicants for a licence are required to meet the conditions laid down in the Motor Vehicles (Driving Licences) Regulations (SI 1981/952). They must be able to read, in good daylight (with the aid of glasses if worn), a registration mark fixed to a motor vehicle at a distance of 75 feet in the case of a registration mark containing letters and figures 3½ inches high or at a distance of 67 feet in the case of a registration mark containing letters and figures 3⅛ inches high. An offence is committed by anyone who drives at any time if his eyesight does not meet this standard under s. 91 of the Road Traffic Act 1972. A further offence is now committed by a licence holder who fails to notify the Licensing Centre when his eyesight falls below this standard or when he has been specifically advised that it is likely to fall below that standard. The obligation to notify disabilities to the Licensing Centre extends in the case of eyesight, to any other defects of vision which affect, or may in time affect, a driver's ability to drive safely.

In practice there is no precise Snellen equivalent to the number plate standard. Recently it was shown that the nearest equivalent on a standard test chart is between 6/9 and 6/12 (Drasdo and Haggerty) but this is not a statutory standard.

## Heavy goods vehicles and public service vehicles driving licences

Applicants are required to reach an uncorrected standard of visual acuity of 6/60 in each eye and have a corrected acuity of at least 6/9 in the better eye and 6/12 in the poorer eye. If their performance is below this standard then they should be referred to an ophthalmologist for advice as to whether they should be allowed to drive. Those drivers who can reach this standard only with spectacles should always carry a spare pair. (The previous recommendations for visual acuity did not mention any minimum standard without glasses.)

Vocational licences are still issued to contact lens wearers and to patients who have had a cataract extraction, and to pseudophakic patients provided that they can meet the uncorrected standard of static acuity of 6/60 in each eye and other requirements laid down above.

## Student and private pilots' licences

1. Full and normal field of vision.
2. A visual acuity of at least 6/12 (20/40; 0.5) in each eye separately with or without correcting glasses. In the case of a correction over plus or minus 5.00 D a specialist's opinion is required.
3. A record should be made of any degree of heterophoria present.
4. The candidate should be able to read Jaeger no. 3 at 30–50 cm or its equivalent at the same distance, with each eye separately, allowing correcting lenses to be worn if it is the usual habit of the candidate to wear such lenses.
5. Contact lenses may be used provided binocular vision is correctable to at least 6/12. Any person wishing to use contact lenses should have a wearing time of several hours a day and should have been wearing lenses for at least six months. A specialist's report should be submitted.
6. Monocular candidates should be referred to the Civil Aviation Authority, Medical Department, CAA House, Kingsway, London WC2B 6TE.
7. If the Ishihara test shows defective colour vision then the Giles–Archer or Holmes–Wright lantern test must be carried out.

Any problems encountered when confronted by a prospective candidate for a private pilot's licence should be directed to the Civil Aviation Authority.

## Professional pilots' licences

The requirements for professional pilots' licences (i.e. ALTP, SCPL and CPL) are:

1. There should be no acute or chronic disease in either eye or adnexae.
2. The fields of vision should be normal.
3. A visual acuity of at least 6/9 (20/30; 0.7) in each eye separately, with or without correcting glasses. If correcting glasses are required, the unaided vision must not be less than 6/60 (20/200; 0.1) and the refractive error must not exceed plus or minus 3.00 D (equivalent spherical error); in addition, a spare pair of suitable lenses should always be carried. In such cases the medical certificate will bear an endorsement noting the requirement to wear correcting glasses.
4. Any degree of heterophoria found in the test should be noted in the candidate's medical record (hyperphoria greater than 1.5△ or esophoria greater than 6△ is not normally accepted).
5. Candidates are required to have accommodation which permits them to read the Faculty of Ophthalmology reading chart N5 or its equivalent at a distance of 30–50 cm with each eye separately, with or without correcting glasses.

6. The wearing of contact lenses is not permitted in professional pilots.
7. The candidate is required to have normal colour vision perception as tested by Ishihara pseudo-isochromatic plates in good daylight; alternatively, he must be able to recognise the colours of signal red, signal green and white using the large and medium apertures of a Giles–Archer lantern at a distance of 20 feet in a darkened room after 10 minutes of dark adaptation.
8. The prescription of corrections for both near and distance vision should be notified.


## Merchant shipping

Merchant shipping sight test standards are laid down in Notice M 1061. The regulation is in two sections.

Section 1 applies to young persons and new entrants about to embark on a career in the fishing industry or on merchant navy vessels.

1. Before embarking on a sea-going career in a desk capacity every young person should undergo a thorough examination in both form and colour vision by an ophthalmologist.
2. A letter test is carried out using Snellen charts, the subject being required to read correctly down to and including line 7 with the better eye and down to and including line 6 with the other eye. This should relate to acuities of 6/6 and 6/7.5.
3. A lantern test is carried out in a darkened room. A series of red, white or green lights are shown either singly through a large aperture or two at a time through small apertures side by side. The candidate is required to name the colours correctly as they appear.
4. During the examination candidates will not be allowed to wear spectacles, contact lenses or glasses of any kind or any other artificial aid to vision. Treatment designed to improve vision temporarily should not be undertaken shortly before the test.

Section 2 applies to candidates for Department of Trade sight tests for a first certificate of competency or higher certificate and voluntary applicants for the sight test other than new entrants to the merchant navy or fishing industry. The sight test may be taken with or without aids (conventional spectacles or contact lenses) at the candidate's option, but different requirements apply to each option.

1. If aids are used:
   (a) the letter test is first carried out without the aids, and the requirement is to read down to and including line 5 with the better eye and down to and including line 3 with the other eye;
   (b) the test is repeated with the aids, the requirement being to read correctly down to and including line 7 with the better eye and down to and including line 6 with the other eye.
2. If the sight test is carried out without aids then the applicant will be required to read down to and including line 7 with the better eye and down to and including line 6 with the other eye.

3. Candidates who have failed a test without aids may apply to retake the test locally with aids after a period of not less than one month.
4. Candidates who have failed a test when not using aids may be re-examined locally without aids after a period of one month.

## Metropolitan police force

The requirement for entry as a constable in the metropolitan police is that the acuity with or without spectacles is at least 6/6 in the good eye and 6/12 in the poorer eye, with a binocular acuity of 6/6 and a minimum unaided vision in each eye of 6/18. The applicant is also required to pass the 14th edition of the Ishihara test plates for colour vision or at least show the 'ability to distinguish the principal colours'.

## British Railways

This group may be divided into the footplate grades (i.e. drivers, secondmen and traction trainees and cleaners) and grades other than footplate grades. In the first group, on entry the applicant is required to have acuities of 6/6 in each eye and 6/6 binocularly with the fogging test with correction and also have normal colour vision. The entrants are required to have re-examinations at regular intervals.

In the second group of grades (i.e. other than footplate grades) the following subsections apply.

1. Class A. These are required to take tests unaided and must have acuities of 6/12 in each eye and binocularly with a fogging test. If the applicant is wearing a visual correction then he or she must have acuities of at least 6/9 in one eye and 6/12 in the other eye, with binocular acuity of 6/9, again with a fogging test; also the glasses must not exceed plus or minus 5.00 D in any meridian. All applicants in this group are required to have normal colour vision. Bifocal lenses are generally permitted but contact lenses are not normally considered suitable. All staff in this group who are likely to use mechanical vehicles or to be on or about the running lines will be subject to re-examination at the age of 40 years and thereafter at five-yearly intervals.
2. Class B – clerical staff. In this group, because of the wide range of employment, the standards laid down are not adhered to so strictly. In general, however, an applicant is required to be able to attain an acuity of 6/12 or better in the better eye and at least 6/36 in the poorer eye with or without spectacles. In addition, a near vision acuity of N5 is required. No significant pathological condition may be present.

In general the spectacle correction should not exceed plus or minus 5.00 D in any meridian, although this is subject to the discretion of the medical officer.

## Definitions of blindness and partial sight

Although this, in terms of registration, does not fall within the scope of the ophthalmic optician/optometrist in practice, a knowledge of the definitions of blindness and partial sight is often useful. An ophthalmic optician/

optometrist may not register a patient as blind; this may be carried out only by an ophthalmic medical practitioner or ophthalmologist.

## *Blindness*

The statutory definition for the purpose of registration as a blind person under s. 64 of the National Assistance Act 1948 is that the person is

'so blind as to be unable to perform any work for which eyesight is essential'.

As a consequency of this two points should be considered:

1. The National Assistance Act 1948 states in the definition 'so blind as to be unable to perform any work . . .' and does not relate to a particular occupation or the person's own occupation.
2. It is only the eyesight which is taken into account; any other bodily or mental infirmities are disregarded.

The principal condition to be considered is the visual acuity with correction, either of each eye separately or of both together. As a definition, however, the use of visual acuity alone is not adequate and therefore three classifications of 'blind' exist at present within the meaning of the legislation:

1. Below 3/60 Snellen acuity. In general a person whose best visual acuity is below 3/60 may be regarded as blind. Often, however, 1/18 is used as the standard and in this case the person is not considered blind unless there is also considerable restriction of the visual field.
2. 3/60 but below 6/60 Snellen acuity. A person with visual acuity of 3/60 but less than 6/60 may be considered blind only if this is accompanied by considerable contraction in the field of view. The person is not, however, considered blind within the meaning of the National Assistance Act 1948 if the visual defect is of long standing and is unaccompanied by any material contraction of the field of vision.
3. 6/60 Snellen acuity or better. A person with 6/60 acuity or better is not normally considered blind. If, however, there is marked contraction of the visual field over the greater part of its extent, and particularly where the contraction appears in the lower part of the field, then the patient may be eligible for registration.

## *Partial sight*

There is no statutory definition of partial sight within the National Assistance Act 1948 but the Department of Health and Social Security has advised that a person who is not blind within the meaning of the 1948 legislation but who is, nevertheless, substantially and permanently handicapped by defective vision whether congenital or through injury or illness does fall within the scope of eligibility for the welfare services with the local authorities are empowered to provide.

The following guidelines are offered when considering whether or not a person should be regarded as partially sighted and when, in the case of a child under 16 years of age, a decision is made as to the type of school recommended.

1. For registration purposes for the provision of welfare services:
   (a) 3/60 to 6/60 with full field;
   (b) up to 6/24 with moderate contraction of the field, opacities in the media or aphakia;
   (c) 6/18 or better with a gross field defect or marked contraction of the whole visual field.
2. For children when deciding appropriate education:
   (a) severe visual disabilities where education in special schools is required, from 3/60 to 6/24 with correction;
   (b) visual impairment where education at ordinary schools is considered suitable if some special consideration is given, better than 6/24 corrected.

The above details should provide a useful background for the most commonly requested vocational requirements. The requirements do, however, vary from time to time and for specific details it may be necessary to contact the relevant governing body.

# 14

# Legal requirements of referral

Patient referral is one of the most important functions of the ophthalmic optician/optometrist in routine practice. Ophthalmic opticians/optometrists act as screeners to detect and send for further investigation those patients with ocular abnormalities. That this screening service works has been demonstrated by a number of articles in recent issues of the *British Journal of Ophthalmology* and other similar journals in which the referral service has been praised with special regard to glaucoma and diabetes. Further evidence for the success of the ophthalmic profession in screening is provided by the diabetic study being conducted by the Bristol Area Health Authority. Preliminary results suggest that the screening service provided by ophthalmic opticians/optometrists in the area is so good that it is better than could normally be expected, and is better and more cost effective than could be achieved by setting up specialised investigative services.

There are therefore very good reasons for the referral service within the general ophthalmic services, and, to aid in the smooth running of the service, there are certain legal requirements placed on the ophthalmic optician/optometrist. Within the general ophthalmic services, under the terms of service for an ophthalmic optician, a patient should be referred to his or her general practitioner for the following specified conditions.

1. When the patient needs treatment beyond the scope of the general ophthalmic services. Within this category would fall orthoptic treatment and the fitting of contact lenses. Obviously this does not mean that the ophthalmic optician/optometrist cannot undertake orthoptics or contact lenses, but if he/she does so it will not be under the health service but under private arrangement between himself/herself and the patient.
2. Where it appears that a patient is suffering from an injury or a non-physiological abnormality of the eye or visual system.
3. Where, after correction and in the absence of visible pathology, a patient's vision does not achieve an acceptable standard. (The standard is generally taken as 6/9 to 6/12, although there are some ophthalmologists who suggest referral if acuity differs between the two eyes by more than one line of letters.)
4. Where a child is attending for the first time and no correction is necessary.
5. Where a further examination is considered necessary within six months.

These five regulations relate to the ophthalmic optician/optometrist under contract to the NHS and providing general ophthalmic services. Failure to comply with these rules could lead to disciplinary action by the family practitioner committee and, ultimately, withdrawal of the practitioner's name from the general ophthalmic services lists.

In addition to the above regulations the GOC have, in fulfilment of the duty laid on them under s. 25(3) of the Opticians Act 1958, published Rules Relating to Injury or Disease of the Eye, embodied in SI 1960/1936. Under the terms of this instrument, where it appears to an ophthalmic optician/optometrist that a patient is suffering from an injury or disease of the eye of which the patient's general medical practitioner may not be aware, the ophthalmic optician/optometrist must report the findings to the general practitioner. Failure to comply with this regulation could lead to a case being brought before the Disciplinary Committee of the GOC, and, if negligence were proved, result in erasure of the opthalmic optician/optometrists's name from the opticians register.

According to the GOC the following steps should be taken when referring a patient to a registered medical practitioner.

1. The ophthalmic optician/optometrist should advise the patient to consult his/her general practitioner.
2. Wherever possible a written report of the findings should be supplied, with an indication of the reasons for suspecting injury or disease. If a report is supplied, it should be on either headed notepaper or form GOS 18. Should it appear that urgent action is required, every effort should be made to contact the general practitioner immediately (e.g. by telephone). If it is not possible to contact the patient's general practitioner then the patient should be sent, in the case of an emergency, to the nearest hospital accident and emergency unit with a letter on headed notepaper indicating the reason for referral. A copy of the letter with any further relevant information should be sent to the patient's general practitioner.
3. If a patient is unwilling or refuses to consult the general practitioner then the ophthalmic optician/optometrist should record the grounds for the patient's refusal on the record card, stress the necessity for the patient to visit the general practitioner and ask the patient to sign the note on the record card as a disclaimer should the possibility of legal action arise at a future date.
4. The rules do not prohibit a registered ophthalmic optician/optometrist from administering whatever services he/she may consider in the best interests of the patient in an emergency situation.

The GOC have defined the terms 'injury or disease', as used in the Opticians Act 1958, to cover conditions which cause or are likely to cause detriment to health or sight, but excluding variations of refraction or normal changes due to age. In addition, the Council have expanded on their rulings in subsequent booklets of guidelines. It is considered that, under SI 1960/1936, the ophthalmic optician/optometrist transfers the authority for dealing with the patient to the general practitioner upon referral. This is interpreted as meaning that the general practitioner should decide whether or not spectacles should be prescribed. The exception to this is in an emergency; for example, where a patient is unable to follow his occupation or is gravely inconvenienced without spectacles the ophthalmic optician/optometrist may make the decision to supply spectacles provided that this is unlikely to prevent the patient from seeking further advice. Generally it is considered the responsibility of the general practitioner to notify the ophthalmic optician/optometrist not to supply spectacles if that is his opinion.

### General referral procedure

There is no set procedure for referral but, under the GOC regulations, the ophthalmic optician/optometrist will normally be expected to write a note, dated and on headed paper, indicating his/her findings and post this to the patient's general practitioner. In some instances referral will be direct to hospital (as an emergency), in which case the general practitioner should be notified by phone, followed by written confirmation describing the reasons for referral. In this direct referral to hospital, a letter should be sent with the patient, which gives the hospital details of the reasons for such referral.

It is generally considered acceptable for the patient to take a letter by hand to the general practitioner. This has certain advantages in that it is not dependent upon the postal services, and the problem of making appointments to coincide with the arrival of the letter is averted. Also the ophthalmic optician/optometrist does not forget to send the letter and the general practitioner does not forget receiving it! The disadvantages are that the patient may not actually visit the general practitioner and also may be tempted to read the letter.

There is no legal or professional obligation to inform the patient of the contents of a referral letter. As a matter of courtesy, however, and to allay fears, it is normally better to inform the patient in general terms of the reasons for referral. This does not mean that the patient is given a diagnosis; under the terms of the NHS an ophthalmic optician/optometrist is a detector of abnormality and not a diagnostician. There is obviously overlap between the two functions, but it is better simply to indicate to the patient that a particular aspect is not normal rather than to give a definite named condition which may be incorrect or which may be subsequently refuted for reasons not apparent at the original examination.

If a patient is referred then spectacles will not normally be dispensed until after the patient's further examination. This works only in emergency cases. In situations where the patient may have to wait several months for a further examination, it is obviously sensible for him to have a current visual correction while he waits, particularly if it achieves an improvement in visual performance or a reduction in severity of symptoms. If a patient is unable to follow his normal occupation or if he is 'gravely inconvenienced' without spectacles then they should be supplied. In the absence of special circumstances, the final decision whether or not to prescribe spectacles rests with the family doctor and not the ophthalmic optician/optometrist. If spectacles are supplied when a patient is referred then it should be made clear to the patient that the spectacles are supplied on a provisional basis and must be cancelled or returned if the general practitioner feels that they should not be supplied.

## Information-only referrals

Since the abolition of Form GOS 1 (used by general practitioners to refer patients to an ophthalmic optician/optometrist), the ophthalmic practitioner has been expected to write to the general practitioner in certain situations which would not constitute a referral. The situations are:

1. Where a patient under the age of 16 years reports for an initial examination and, following the examination, no correction is given.
2. Where a patient reports for an eye examination and a further examination within six months is recommended.

A further, much less defined, area for writing to the general practitioner is in cases of chronic pathology. Although the ophthalmic optician/optometrist is not expected to diagnose, there is a need to detect and refer cases of abnormality. If this were strictly adhered to then the hospital eye service would be unable to cope, even allowing for an effective screening service by the general practitioner. In the case of cataract, for example, there are two arguments for referral:

1. The patient should be referred at the first sign of an abnormality.
2. The patient should be referred only when the vision has deteriorated to a level likely to seriously affect his daily routine.

Strictly, the first course of action should be followed, and the merit of this action is that the patient will have a full ophthalmological investigation while the fundus is still easily seen. In many hospital clinics, however, consultants are not keen to have their time taken up with this type of examination. On a practical level, a letter to the general practitioner, noting the presence of early cataract, stressing that it does not interfere with vision and suggesting re-examination at regular intervals to monitor the progression, is a much more sensible approach. The system has more flexibility, and the general practitioner can decide whether to see the patient or simply to agree to the regular monitoring of the condition. This is the true meaning of screening as applied to the ophthalmic optician/optometrist and is an important aspect of the general health care. It is important to remember, however, that to work efficiently the general practitioner must have respect for the ophthalmic optician/optometrist's ability, and the ophthalmic optician/optometrist must communicate all relevant information to the general practitioner.

## Layout of referral letters

Referral to the patient's general practitioner should be either by submission of a form GOS 18 or on headed notepaper showing the practice address and the principal partners. In many areas, if a GOS 18 is used then a reply is sent from the local ophthalmologist to the ophthalmic optician/optometrist who referred; this is less likely when headed notepaper is used.

When using headed notepaper the letter should be dated and should begin with the patient's full name and address. It should contain details of history and symptoms, vision and visual correction with best acuities for distance and near, together with any previous acuities and the date recorded. The reasons for referral (e.g. motility problems, poor acuity, abnormal fundus) should be clearly stated. Finally, the letter should be signed by the ophthalmic optician/optometrist and a duplicate of the letter retained with the patient's record. A further copy of the letter should be sent to the general practitioner for the patient's file. This last step is of great importance as a form of protection should there ever be the suggestion that no action was taken.

It is extremely important that ophthalmic opticians/optometrists keep adequate case records giving details of ocular examinations. If the eye is examined and found to be completely clear of abnormality it is just as important that this be recorded as the recording of the presence of abnormality. A practitioner's protection in any legal action is his case record and it is important therefore that it is given priority. Further details about case records are given in Appendix 1.

# Part II

# Management in Optometric Practice

**15**

# Types of practice, layout and equipment

Unless an optometrist is a locum tenens then, apart from taking clinical decisions regarding the eye care and welfare of his patients, he must also be prepared to make management decisions regarding the welfare of his practice. This may range from small day-to-day matters such as when to order more stationery if he is a manager in a multiple, to momentous plans such as opening a new branch if he is sole proprietor. This chapter will cover these plus other 'policy' decisions entailed in setting up and running a successful optometric practice.

## Types of practice

With the advent of 'consumerism' and other pressures a choice has to be made as to whether a practice is to have a 'commercial' or a 'clinical' emphasis. It would appear that the days of the small practitioner with a couple of dusty frames in his shop window and the bare minimum of diagnostic equipment are nearly over (at least in the big towns), and a good job too. However, whether the patient's best interests are served by shop windows and waiting room walls full of spectacle frames or the availability and *regular use* of comprehensive clinical equipment is an argument destined to rage as long as optometry is practised. Whatever your persuasion, you must broadly decide which image you wish to project to your future patients. This in turn will dictate the type of patient you are likely to attract: the clinically orientated practice will tend to book the rather more discerning (and possibly more time-consuming!) person who has been recommended by either another patient or a local doctor, whereas the commercially orientated will tend to be frequented by the casual patient who is 'shopping around', as usually recommended by the popular media. The situation now is further complicated by the legalisation of unregistered spectacle retailers, although the public are more likely to confuse these with overtly commercial practices rather than the more dignified office or house practice.

It is probably harder work in the early days to start a brass plate practice. Each patient seen is a public relations exercise. He has come in for advice about his eyes, not a closer look at the frame he has seen in the window (or advertised in the paper or on TV). You must be prepared to listen attentively and sympathetically to long stories and lists of symptoms, and sort out the relevant details. You have then to produce, at the very least, a satisfactory explanation for the symptoms and also, it is hoped, a course of treatment to relieve or alleviate them, whether by refractive help, exercises, medication or referral. This takes a lot of time – and time is money. In the UK, where the NHS can not, or will not, pay a reasonable fee to cover the time, expertise and equipment necessary to complete a comprehensive eye examination and do not pay for increasingly more sophisticated examinations or advice, the early months of starting a practice will entail work primarily for one's reputation, not turnover. The rewards come later, in the form of a solid patient base on which to build further, together with enhanced professional status, satisfaction and financial security. Patients who like and trust you as a person will remain loyal and return to seek your advice in the future, recommending you to their friends and family no matter what the latest consumer report or full page advertisement in the local newspaper may urge.

### Premises

To some extent the type of accommodation is related to the type of practice. A clinically orientated practice would not be situated most cost effectively in the high street where the rents and rates are highest. Patients will be consulting the optometrist for his individual reputation (not his latest window display) and will be prepared to seek him out on a less busy thoroughfare where, incidentally, the parking is likely to be much easier. Space for expansion is usually non-existent in a modern shop unit and, if the practice is to flourish, a disruptive move will eventually be necessary.

  Most small towns have an area where other professional practices such as dentists, accountants and solicitors are to be found. These are usually situated in large Victorian-type properties which are ideal for expansion as the optometric practice grows and more room is required for another colleague, clinical tests room, contact lens instruction room and so on. Very successful conversions can be made of shop premises, as will be discussed later, but the effect on overheads must always be borne in mind. Of course, if the freehold of the property can be obtained, then at least one is immune from the disastrous rent rises which could eventually force the practice off the high street. It goes without saying that the higher the overheads then the higher the fees charged and/or the less professional time it is possible to spend with patients and still remain solvent – a situation unsatisfactory for practitioner and patient alike. More will be said later on the question of overheads and the use of optometric assistants who can be skilfully used to improve patient care in providing more extensive examinations and yet reduce costs.

  In some instances overheads can be dramatically reduced by sharing accommodation. This is a common arrangement in the USA where one purpose-built 'professional building' surrounded by plenty of parking may house several medical specialties, a dentist and an optometrist. Not only can the heating, lighting, cleaning and so on be shared but so can the reception. In this way a practice builds up more rapidly with interprofessional referrals and exposure to potential patients consulting the other practitioners on the premises. The nearest to this in the UK are the new health centres springing up round the country. However, greater care must be exercised before any agreements are made to practise from one of these, as problems have arisen relating to the ownership of the records and goodwill. In any case the advice of the Association of Optical Practitioners should be sought.

Part-time optometric practices can share premises with other part-time professional practices with great success. The author shares buildings with a dentist in one local village and a solicitor in another, to everyone's advantage. It would otherwise be totally uneconomic to provide a service in either village.

The last type of practice to be considered is the Cinderella of the service: hospital work. Although great advances have been made in hospital salaries for optometrists in recent years, there is still a large gap between them and the income from a practice combining general ophthalmic services and private work.

It has been said that those optometrists who work in the hospital service come in two roughly equal groups. They are either philanthropists with more regard for their specialty than their standard of living or they are poor examples of their profession, unable to make a living on the 'outside'. Since the only optometrist some ophthalmologists ever meet is the one in their hospital department, it is likely that the latter group may be responsible for some of the misunderstandings between the two professions. Nevertheless, if you are totally clinically and research orientated, and are lucky enough to find yourself working in an eye department with progressive ophthalmologists, there is little doubt that this can be one of the most rewarding ways in which to practise optometry. Nearly all of one's undergraduate training such as subnormal vision management, fundus photography, etc. can be put into practice, with the opportunity to carry out more advanced techniques as they become available. Unfortunately, hospital optometrists are sometimes employed to undertake refraction only, especially those employed on a sessional basis, so be very careful to ensure that the scope of your proposed activities is to your liking before committing yourself. If you are about to leave university, it must be pointed out that several hospitals have serious deficiencies as a training ground for a full-time pre-registration year. Sometimes routines such as tonometry, visual fields, blood pressure measurement and even the prescribing of prisms may never be undertaken by the student. These are apart from areas such as dispensing and occupational visual welfare which are deficiencies more likely to be anticipated. So undergraduates beware: if you choose a full-time hospital pre-registration post you will almost certainly have to make up for lack of experience in entire subjects by obtaining practical experience elsewhere. Do remember that as far as relationships with the medical profession are concerned, when working in a hospital *you* are an ambassador for our profession, and professions judge other professions by their mistakes!

Finally, loose relationships do exist between optometrists and ophthalmologists in private practice and may prove very satisfactory from a professional point of view. For example, the optometrist discusses the optical consequences of a cataract extraction to the patient prior to the operation and prescribes and dispenses a suitable optical appliance afterwards. Of course, certain legalities should be sorted out first, such as ownership of records and goodwill, but a visit to a solicitor is all that is required.

## Layout of premises, fittings and equipment

Naturally this section is almost totally dependent on the physical properties of the accommodation. However, let us look at the ideal, and compromises can be made as necessary.

### External appearance

Even if you feel a shop window containing frames is important, studies such as those by the New Zealand Optometrical Association (1969) and Simmonds (1981) have shown that about 95 per cent of patients who visit a particular practice rather than any other do so because they have been referred by another patient or another practitioner, are simply returning for a follow-up visit or just find the location convenient. In other words, apart from projecting a 'shoptician' image, totally inappropriate for a graduate clinical profession, window displays of frames are economically unsound. The time and expense of arranging, cleaning and altering them is not cost effective. It is sometimes argued that, when starting a new practice in certain locations such as shopping areas, a token display of three or four spectacle frames is necessary to indicate your presence. This is not true; a modern, new front to the premises, together with the name and qualifications of the optometrist attending prominently displayed, will do the job far better. In this way, no emphasis is placed on what may be obtained therein other than advice about vision and the eyes. Spectacle frames are the 'sugar on the pill' of one form of treatment for visual difficulties. If you project them as your *raison d'être*, then, as consumerism and advertising grow apace, you will be judged by the cost of your frames compared with those in the local supermarket instead of your expertise and dedication to visual welfare.

If you are starting or taking over a practice in shop-type premises, there are many ways of modifying the exterior to produce the desired professional effect. Some of these are illustrated in *Figure 15.1*, taken from *Design for Optometric Premises* published by the New Zealand Optometrical Association (1969). The NZOA voted to outlaw shop window displays by 1972.

### Reception area

The first impression of your practice is gained here. The surroundings should purvey a feeling of quiet, friendly efficiency (reception staff dressed in identical clothes help to promote this atmosphere). For this reason it is a mistake to separate reception from the waiting room. Nervous patients enjoy a chat and reassurance while they are waiting for their appointment, and, if you are running late, a sympathetic receptionist can salvage your goodwill. There must be plenty of comfortable seating and current magazines available. A custom-made desk or 'counter' with various pigeon holes and drawers is often worth the expense to hold the NHS forms, rubber stamps,

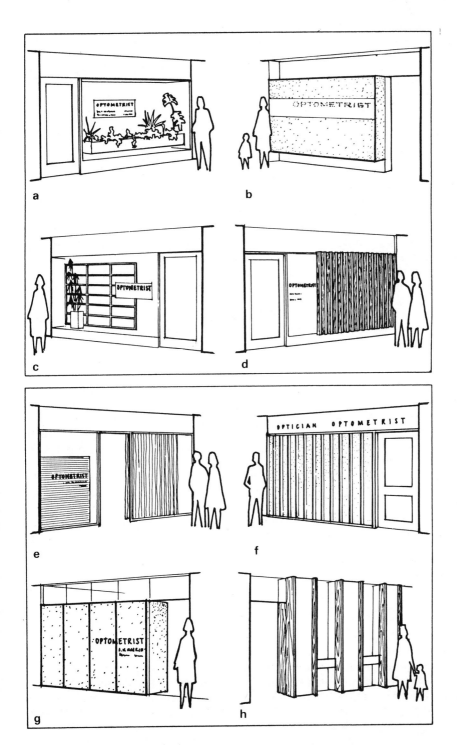

*Figure 15.1* Some examples of exteriors of premises. (a) Plants providing a partial screen; (b) existing window sandblasted, providing a partial screen; (c) fibreglass and timber screen; (d) timber louvres in front of the window; (e) partitioning and curtaining as a partial screen; (f) ribbed obscuring glass panel; (g) exposed aggregate panels; (h) timber frames with glass panels to provide partial screen. (Reproduced, by kind permission of the New Zealand Optometrical Association Inc, from NZOA, 1969)

jobs awaiting collection, contact lens solutions and other paraphernalia associated with optometric practice. A rack or folder containing literature for patients should be available and well stocked with material to promote all our areas of expertise, from paediatric optometry to the provision of special aids for the elderly. More will be said in Chapter 19 concerning public relations, an area which many in the optometric profession have sadly neglected in the past. Suffice it to say that every patient seen must be a PR exercise. Every one must leave the practice knowing much more about our profession and their vision than when they came in.

The reception desk is the hub of the practice and as such must be the centre of communications. It is essential that there be two-way contact between here and every other working area in the practice. This may be by a system of bells or buzzers but the best method is by telephone so that outside callers can be put through to professional staff if necessary and the practitioner can ask for assistance or information without leaving his consulting room or the receptionist her desk (which is usually where the till is kept!). In fact, anything but the smallest practice will benefit from two telephone lines, one being ex-directory so that outside calls to prescription houses, doctors and so on can be made without using the published number. A continually engaged line is not a practice builder nor soothing to a contact lens patient in a busy telephone box who desperately wants advice on an acute problem.

While on the subject of telephones, an answering machine giving telephone numbers to contact in an emergency is rarely abused in the author's experience. It also enables patients to cancel appointments or to leave other messages outside normal office hours and enables you to make announcements regarding opening hours and holidays when you are closed (*see also* Chapter 19).

The patient's records, whether on computer or conventional filing cards, must be readily accessible from the desk, and the receptionist must be encouraged to look up the record whenever a patient makes an enquiry. Instant familiarity with a patient's personal and clinical details creates a good impression and promotes an efficient response. Brief details of the conversation should always be written on the record, too, in order to avoid confusion and contradiction later.

### Fitting room

A separate fitting room for spectacle collection should be provided if at all possible. If not, it should be combined with the dispensing room rather than the waiting area. Few people like the position of their ears discussed, or their eligibility for financial help from the DHSS considered, while sitting next to a stranger. It is also a handy place in which to whisk patients who are having trouble adapting to their new spectacles out of sight and earshot of the next appointment.

The room must contain a suitable number of chairs, a table, hand and wall mirrors and a near reading chart. Frame-adjusting tools including a heater, a range of pliers and files must be available. It is recommended that major adjustments such as the filing out and polishing of bridges be carried out in the workshop, away from the patient, or he may conclude that the frame or facial measurements were incorrectly recorded or the wrong frame ordered.

## Workshop

In most practices this room is where larger adjustments and repairs are carried out, although in some practices it will contain some or all of the facilities of a prescription house. Obviously, minor repairs and adjustments must be part of the service offered by every optometrist. A patient would not expect his spectacles to be sent away to have a new screw fitted. How comprehensive to make the facilities must be the decision of the individual practitioner. On the one hand, making a solder repair on a frame while the patient waits is undoubtedly first-class service; on the other hand, it is totally non-cost-effective if the optometrist does it himself, apart from engendering the wrath of the delayed next appointment. There is also the consideration of a second-rate job as, in this example, there may not be replating equipment available. It would appear, therefore, that unless one is prepared to do the job properly and set up a workshop offering comprehensive facilities with possibly two glazers, then all but minor repairs are better left to the experts. Two glazers are suggested because the local prescription houses are unlikely to help you out during holidays or illness when you are in competition with them! The pros and cons of optometrists doing their own glazing and the financial consequences have been discussed by Sasieni (1981a) whilst Klein (1981) extols all the virtues he has found by adding this facility to his practice.

If one intends to offer only a comprehensive adjustment and simple repair service to one's patients then the following fittings and equipment should be considered.

1. Suitable table/desk and chairs.
2. NHS frame spares (in all available colours and dimensions).
3. Assorted pads, bridges and end-tips for GF frames.
4. Box of odd fronts and sides (acquired over the years for emergency repairs – never throw anything away!).
5. Screws for every model of frame you use or have used, in small transparent vials plus an adhesive such as Loctite or nail varnish to secure them better next time.
6. Slip-on side shields for eye protection.
7. Spare pads plus acetone for building up saddle bridges to improve the fit on awkward noses.
8. Reel of nylon for Supra repairs and for 'sewing' broken bridges as a temporary measure.
9. Bench or well-supported shelf on which to mount: a small vice; Clavulus* (device for repinning and tightening joints); electric buffing wheel; electric drill and spare drills for drilling out screws and sewing broken bridges; frame heater.
10. Assorted optical pliers, screw drivers, small hammer, fine and medium files, razor blades, oil, fine and medium emery cloth, tape for inserting lenses into Supras.

* A multipurpose tool obtainable from many optical equipment suppliers.

11. Focimeter.
12. Ultrasonic cleaner or old tooth brush and washing-up liquid.
13. Frame rule.
14. Order books.
15. File of jobs on order.

If you fit contact lenses, you may wish to have an area in the workshop for checking and modification. This is covered later under 'Special equipment'.

### Consulting room

This is the optometrist's domain and is probably best decorated to suit his own personality. At one extreme we have the ultraclinical, almost surgical, approach where the optometrist wears a white coat and resides in a strictly functional consulting room with white-painted walls and easy-wipe surfaces and plastic tiles on the floor. At the other extreme there is the more 'homely' approach where the practitioner wears a suit or even casual clothes and decorates his consulting room more like a comfortable office. There will be wallpaper, carpet and even candelabra and wall-lights instead of the ubiquitous fluorescent tubes. A couple of well chosen pictures on the wall can emphasise informality. The author prefers the latter approach in order to help the patient to relax as if he were in somebody's sitting room. It should also be remembered that the optometrist may spend 30–40 hours a week for the next 30–40 years in the consulting room, so it may as well have the odd touch of luxury (electrically operated curtains cost less than a retinoscope!).

A wash hand basin is essential for use after the external examination and for contact lens practice. An air conditioner is very welcome in a hot summer; these usually now incorporate a heating element which may be used to supplement the central heating in winter. A desk and comfortable chair should be provided, together with one or two other chairs for relatives or friends who may accompany the patient. Your favourite optometric books should be readily available for reference in a bookcase.

No two optometrists would draw up an identical list of clinical equipment they would like in their consulting rooms. Sasieni (1981b) has produced an exhaustive catalogue of essential, desirable and optional equipment which has helped in the construction of the following inventory, from which you may like to make your personal list:

1. Patient's chair and refractionist's stool.
2. Distance chart incorporating your favourite panels and mirror.
3. Children's/illiterate's distance and near vision test (e.g. Sheridan–Gardner, Titmus Fly, Lang Stereotest).
4. Near vision charts.
5. Children's near fixation device.
6. Trial case and trial frame.
7. Spring occluder.
8. Crossed-cylinders.
9. Refractor head (phoropter).
10. Ophthalmoscope.

11. Retinoscope.
12. Hand slit-lamp and loupe.
13. PD rule.
14. Near point rule.
15. Spherometer.
16. Near muscle balance test.
17. Muscle imbalance compensation tests (distance and near).
18. Slit-lamp with Goldmann tonometer and camera attachment.
19. Keratometer.
20. Instrument column wired for central control of room lighting, curtains, etc.
21. Focimeter.
22. Simulated TV test and motorist's test.
23. Ishihara colour vision test.
24. Lantern colour vision test.
25. Stereoscopic vision test.
26. Drugs cabinet with selection of mydriatics, cycloplegics, miotics, local anaesthetics, stains, therapeutic drops and ointment, foreign body instrument, muscle hook, tweezers, pad and bandage, etc.
27. Folder containing NHS and private fees and charges, visual standards for various occupations, etc.

In the following section concerning clinical test rooms, equipment is included which many optometrists would prefer in their consulting rooms. However, if you wish to consider the use of optometric assistants (*see* Chapter 16) and delegate various procedures and measurement determination to them, then a clinical tests room is almost essential.

### Clinical tests room

If you can afford the space, this room is most desirable. If you employ an optometric assistant, he/she can complete any supplementary tests you may require while you proceed with the next patient. This avoids getting behind with appointments or having to book the patient in again. Therefore the equipment listed is related to procedures which may safely and efficiently be delegated to your optometric assistant.

1. Desk with drawers containing spare stationery.
2. Patient's chair.
3. Chair for relative or friend.
4. Non-contact tonometer.
5. Visual field screener.
6. Bjerrum screen with Juler stimuli projection.
7. Standard arc or Goldmann bowl perimeter.
8. Schirmer strips for tear flow estimation.
9. Electronic sphygmomanometer.
10. Amsler charts.
11. Automatic refractor.
12. Fundus camera.

## Dispensing room

If space permits, frames, demonstration lenses, etc. should be kept in a closed room. Exposing patients to appliances before their examination is like putting the cart before the horse and does not promote the 'eye care before eyewear' image which should be the aim of every ethical optometrist. In a small branch practice, where the waiting room may have to double as the dispensing room, frames may still be kept out of sight in cabinets. You may wish to choose your list from the following.

1. Fitting table(s).
2. Patient's chair(s).
3. Fitter's chair(s).
4. Relative or friend's chair(s).
5. Face rules.
6. Frame rules.
7. Lens rules.
8. Suitable mirrors.
9. Folder containing NHS and private fees and charges, together with information on the powers and blank sizes of all the lenses currently available and sizes and colours of all the frames you stock.
10. Catalogues of frames not actually stocked but from which patients may wish to select frames on approval.
11. Display cases with frames separated into: complete NHS range; metal frames; male plastics frames; female plastics frames; children's frames; safety frames; special frames (e.g. billiard spectacles, swimming goggles, monocles, lorgnettes, make-up spectacles, recumbent spectacles, etc.).
12. Trays of demonstration lenses separated into glass bifocals and multifocals, plastics bifocals and multifocals, glass tint samples, plastics tint samples, special lenses (e.g. chevasse, lenticulated, etc.).
13. Photochromic lens demonstrator.
14. Supplementary Benefit forms, stationery for written estimates.

Careful attention must be paid to the lighting in the dispensing room. This is the one room in the practice where windows letting in natural light are an asset. It enables the colours of frames, tints and their cosmetic effect to be judged most accurately. Failing windows, colour-balanced lighting is available which will do the job almost as well.

Many patients with moderate to high prescriptions, who are therefore unable to see themselves clearly when trying on frames, are not happy to rely on the advice of others. The simplest way to cater for this problem is a set of clip-in spherical lenses (obtained commercially) in one-dioptre steps. The most sophisticated way is to record the new appearance on a videotape, then play it back while the patient watches wearing his/her old spectacles.

## Contact lens instruction room

If you spend much more than about a fifth of your time engaged in contact lens work, a contact lens instruction room is a cost-effective essential. A clinical assistant, well trained in contact lenses (*see* Chapter 17 for training), can undertake the teaching of contact lens handling, use of solutions and eye and lens care, etc. while you are examining the next patient. It is best if the particular assistant is present during the fitting of the patient, as will be described later, because any special instructions regarding lens material, wearing time build-up, and so on can be discussed then. As regards the contents of the room itself, the essentials are:

1. Wash hand basin.
2. Table and matt white laminate top.
3. Table mirrors.
4. Two or more chairs (depending on number of patients/spectators).
5. Storage for comprehensive range of solutions, cases and care systems.
6. Contact lens instruction booklets and leaflets.

Other useful items are a wall chart or book with pictures illustrating eye complications of contact lens wear and the appearance of soiled and damaged lenses. A picture is worth a thousand words when it comes to emphasising the importance of care and hygiene in contact lens wear.

Opinions vary as to how many potential contact lens patients may be instructed at once. One well known optometrist in the USA has his assistants train four new patients simultaneously. His argument is that they learn from each other's mistakes. However, there are logistics problems: as more and more different materials come onto the market, so the assistant must either ensure that the particular 'class' all have the same type of lenses or keep stopping to explain the different handling techniques, care regimens and build-up times to the individuals present. On the other hand, if you undertake much hospital work, you will often feel the need to instruct the spouse or another relative of the patient as well, in case help is required in handling the lenses as in the typical case of the postcataract/aphakic patient with arthritis.

In the final analysis, the wishes of your assistant regarding the number of patients to be instructed at a time is paramount. In the author's experience this has always been one-to-one.

## Office

This is the one room which the patient will never enter. It will probably also have several other functions such as store room and tea room as well, unless you are particularly well off for space. This is not to say that an effort should not be made to try to keep it tidy, although clearing up may most efficiently be left to the end of the day.

In here, patients' spectacles are neutralised, jobs are ordered and checked, the financial records of the practice are stored and the book-keeping is carried on. It is also a place to which one can retire if necessary to discuss patients or policy, so it is a good idea to have a couple of easy chairs besides all the usual office furniture.

## Special equipment

The practice concerned may undertake routine refractions and dispensings only, provide a complete family eye care service, or specialise in certain areas. If either of the last two options applies then certain other specialised equipment must also be contemplated.

*Contact lenses*

Besides the items listed under 'Consulting room' above, the practitioner must also consider:

1. Ultraviolet or Burton lamp.
2. Radiuscope.
3. Measuring micrometer.
4. Thickness gauge.
5. Lens-modifying equipment.
6. Binocular inspection microscope.
7. Eye moulding and casting equipment.
8. Fitting sets.
9. Contact lens solutions.
10. Contact lens trolley.

Consideration should also be given to the concept of stock lenses. This is most easily accomplished with soft lenses when a stock of about 200 of one manufacturer's lenses will fit the majority of potential soft lens patients. The best possible lens replacement service can be offered in this way since duplicate lenses are normally available immediately.

It remains only to decide which lens design you wish to fit as a 'bread and butter' soft lens in your practice. Of course, you will need several other fitting sets as well for those patients who do not suit your chosen stock design or who require extended-wear, toric, tinted, multifocal or other special lenses.

*Partial sight management*

In addition to the normal consulting room equipment, certain other items are essential unless you are going to provide no more than the local chemist's shop in the form of magnifying glasses. Optical aids necessary are:

1. Hand-held monoculars and binoculars.
2. A range of hand-held specialist and self-illuminated magnifiers.
3. Chest-borne and head-borne magnifiers.
4. LVA evaluation set (e.g. Stigmat, Keeler).

Although this is not a textbook on technique, it should be pointed out that many practitioners do not seem to appreciate the value of high reading additions (+6.00 or even more) with prisms in conjunction with an Anglepoise or similar lamp, instead of the more complicated (and more expensive) aids listed above.

Many other items are useful in order to demonstrate how everyday life may be made easier for the partially sighted. For instance: large-number dials for telephones from British Telecom; playing cards with large symbols from the RNIB; typoscopes for writing cheques, addressing letters and reading, free from some of the larger banks; large peaked caps (often used by golfers) for cutting down glare from the sun encountered by patients with cataracts.

It need hardly be said that up-to-date information must be available concerning the visual standards for various jobs, and the degree of sight loss necessary for inclusion on the Partially Sighted Register or the Blind Register, together with the advantages (and disadvantages) of such registration.

Finally, many practices operate a try-it-and-see (*sic*) system whereby patients borrow aids to try in their own homes or places of work where they have more time to evaluate their efficacy. If the patient likes the appliance, it is replaced with a new one, the patient pays and the borrowed item is put back in the pool of loan aids for use by another patient. In this way the practitioner does not end up with a cupboard full of scratched and damaged aids and the patient does not have to pay for something which is of no use to him.

## Orthoptic treatment

There are as many different collections of orthoptic equipment as there are practitioners carrying out orthoptic treatment, and any list would cause controversy. However, any inventory must include an instrument to determine the muscle(s) at fault (e.g. Hess screen), a test for abnormal retinal correspondence (ARC) (e.g. Bagolini lenses), a test for eccentric fixation (e.g. Haidinger's brushes), an instrument for the assessment of the angle of deviation (e.g. prism bar) and some instruments for treatment both at home and in the practice (e.g. synoptophore, Holmes stereoscope and Pigeon Cantonnet stereoscope (PCS)).

For further advice, the reader is referred to a standard text on orthoptics.

## Industrial and occupational vision

Mention has already been made (in the section on the dispensing room) of safety frames, and most optometrists would consider the provision of protective eyewear to be a non-specialised part of their everyday work. However, some practitioners wish to specialise to the extent of becoming consultants in this field and find themselves visiting factories and offices, discussing with management their obligations under the law towards their employees. From this follows advice to both management and employees on how vision may be used most efficiently in the working environment. This will involve the measurement of light levels requiring a lux meter, the possible creation of eye hazard areas, the correct placement of VDUs and supplementary lighting. The lending of a visual screener from your practice to pick up potential candidates for a prescription visual aid or protective eyewear also shows proficient organisation on the part of the practitioner, especially if he takes time to explain to the medical or safety officer what the screener is designed to measure and its operation.

If one is given the privilege of setting up a scheme in a firm from scratch, there are several points which must be appreciated by both management and optometrist:

1. The optometrist must be paid as a consultant, with the fee related to the time spent advising the firm.
2. All referred employees must be free to visit the practitioner of their choice.
3. Except in the most unusual circumstances, all referrals must be examined in the chosen optometrist's own consulting rooms and not at their place of work.

The Occupational Visual Welfare Group of the AOP has done a great deal of work in this area and will be pleased to provide extensive information and advice to any members approached by a firm or interested in this specialty.

*Domiciliary visits*

Again, most conscientious optometrists would consider this part of everyday practice. However, there are some extra pieces of equipment which may be worth considering if this is likely to form a significant part of your work:

1. Portable self-illuminated chart.
2. Portable visual field screener (e.g. Woolf Scotoma Screener).
3. Portable tonometer (e.g. Perkin's Applanation).
4. Domiciliary trial case.
5. Suitcase with trays to hold frame samples.
6. Portable focimeter.

Once you gain a reputation for providing a domiciliary service, it is possible that some patients will request a visit even when they can manage to get to the practice. To discourage this, your receptionist should explain to the patient that not only is it possible to do a more thorough examination at the practice with *all* the equipment at the practitioner's disposal but also a fee will be charged for the visit (which is likely to be substantially more than the taxi fare).

## Compromises

As was said at the beginning of this section, the demarcation of our work and responsibilities into activities carried on in special rooms is likely to be possible for only a few of us, whether for financial or space reasons or both. However, many compromises are obvious. For example, in a small one-day-a-week country practice, the reception area, fitting room, workshop and office will probably all occupy the same room, whilst in many one-optometrist full-time practices the consulting room and clinical tests room will be one and the same.

In order to utilise space to the maximum, it may be necessary to have your consulting room in the basement or on the first floor or higher. In this case a relatively inexpensive stair lift such as those in use in old people's homes should be installed or you will not be able to provide a service in your practice for those members of the community unable to manage stairs.

I have aimed at the ideal for a modern, efficient practice with several optometrists and optometric assistants. With this in mind, this section should enable the setting up of a new practice or redesigning of an existing one along professional cost-effective lines.

*Note* If you wish to practise within the NHS then your local optical committee has the power to ensure that you have certain minimum facilities before you may contract formally with your family practitioner committee to provide general ophthalmic services (*see* Chapter 2).

## Decor

Once a practice is thriving, it is very easy, through familiarity, not to notice the wear and tear on the decorations, fixtures and fittings. Therefore, make a point of occasionally going round the practice when it is closed and sitting where patients sit. Look around you and see if the surroundings still look fresh and efficient. If not, it is time to consider refurbishing or replacing equipment and calling in the decorators!

## Security

The problem of security must unfortunately be taken very seriously, both within the practice (the staff must not be exposed to any avoidable temptation, for their own protection) and from without. The latter includes not only the obvious risks involved outside practice hours when there is nobody on the premises but also petty theft of frames during open hours – a problem likely to become more widespread with the deregistration of spectacle frame supply.

A thorough introduction into this specialist area of practice management may be obtained by contacting the local police station and asking their crime prevention officer to visit you. Particular considerations for optometric practices together with some useful addresses have been detailed by Noir (1984).

# 16

# Duties of receptionists and optometric assistants

Besides the eye examination and any subsequent treatment which may be necessary, many other activities take place in the day-to-day running of an optometric practice as in any other business. This includes the keeping of accounts, stock control, cleaning and so on. Chapters 16 and 17 outline those functions and responsibilities, both clinical and otherwise, which could or should be delegated by the optometrist. This chapter is mainly concerned with the selection, employment and training of optometric assistants. Since the concept of the utilisation of optometric assistants is still relatively novel to many British optometrists, it will be covered in some detail. However, never let it be forgotten that the optometrist is always responsible for the actions and omissions of his assistants even though he may not be directly supervising them.

As the vast majority of non-professional staff working in optometric practices in Britain are female, this section will refer to them as such. There is, of course, no reason why men should not be similarly employed, just as there are many women optometrists.

The history of ophthalmic optics is one of ever-increasing delegation, which probably began with the advent of prescription houses. There are some optometrists who delegate little more than the making of appointments, and even type their own reports. At the other extreme we have practices where carefully in-house trained staff carry out, *under supervision*, many of the procedures which some optometrists may feel cannot, or should not, be delegated.

## Why train optometric assistants?

### Better service to the patient

Ideally the optometrist should carry out all the tests and procedures himself. However, there are time and financial factors which make this impossible, except within a training institution. Unless alternative arrangements are made to carry out some parts of a complete examination, they must simply be left out, with the consequent lowering of standards of service to the patient.

### More extensive examination of the patient

As new, more sophisticated and time-consuming procedures become available, such as pachymetry, ocular photography, tear film break-up time, etc., the optometrist can delegate more to his optometric assistant(s) and hence does not have to work faster and faster to fit more and more into a given appointment time. By delegating some procedures to a trained assistant, he provides an ever more extensive examination of his patient for little more of his professional time.

### More time for non-delegated routines

Routines such as subjective examination, retinoscopy, slit-lamp biomicroscopy and ophthalmoscopy can be completed in a more relaxed fashion. This also leaves more time for the evaluation of the results and subsequent explanation and advice to the patient.

### More time for the optometrist

More time is left for other duties such as practice administration, occupational visual welfare and continuing education at courses, conferences and in reading journals and books such as this!

### Higher patient load per optometrist

More patients can be cared for by a single optometrist and in a *more thorough way* than before. This is an important point for several reasons:

1. There is a decreasing number in the optometric profession.
2. There is a greater demand for optometric services. DHSS figures show there were 6.45 million eye examinations in England and Wales in 1970. By 1983 this had risen to 9.56 million. This is a 32.5 per cent increase for a similar number of practitioners.
3. A higher practice income is required for the new generations of microchip equipment currently being developed both for eye examinations and to improve office efficiency by computerisation. It might also be said that more income is required to pay for the advertising of our services, which the consumer organisations obviously do not expect us to pass onto the patient.

### Enhanced practitioner satisfaction and professional status

As all the above factors can only lead to more thorough and extensive eye examinations, together with a more relaxed and professionally fulfilled practitioner, he is likely to feel more satisfied at the end of the day.

A side effect of employing optometric assistants in the author's experience is the increased professional status of the optometrist in the eyes of the patients. It would appear that the more 'important' a professional person is in our society, the more he employs a support team to gather information for him.

## Terminology

Many titles have been suggested for these non-professional members of staff, such as optometric nurses, optometric aides, paraoptometrics (USA), etc. However, the author suggests the following classification:

1. Optometric receptionist.
2. Optometric (dispensing) assistant.
3. Optometric (clinical) assistant.

## Differences between receptionists and assistants

These are easily delineated by separating the administrative duties from the technical duties. The optometric receptionist is purely administrative, whereas optometric assistants have a more technical function.

## Optometric receptionist

Your optometric receptionist must be made to feel that her job is as important as any other in the practice, which it is. She is the key to a successful practice, being the first person with whom the patient comes into contact and the link between the practitioner, the assistants and the public. As such, she must be cheerful, sympathetic, intelligent and unflappable – there are not many about!

She has to make vital decisions such as whether a request to see the optometrist by a patient should be treated as an emergency and be seen immediately or whether an appointment should be made in the usual way. Her duties may be outlined as follows.

### *Reception duties*

*Making appointments*

This is not as simple as it sounds. Apart from judging the urgency of the request, the patient must be asked his name and address, how long it is since he last had an eye examination and must be told to bring with him any visual correction, including magnifiers, if used. If the patient has been to the practice before, his record should be retrieved from the file before the appointment is confirmed in case there are some cryptic comments from previous examinations which may influence the timing of the appointment. For instance, 'talks a lot' (in code, or course!) should suggest to the receptionist that she should not offer the last slot in the morning or afternoon or you will not get any lunch or reach your evening meeting on time. Telephone technique is also vital, but is discussed in detail in Chapter 19.

*Filing*

This is sometimes treated as being rather boring and of secondary importance. But what is the use of keeping records if you cannot find them? It should be impressed upon your receptionist that filing is one of her more vital duties. Hours can be wasted searching for mis-filed records and patients do not take kindly to being 'lost'.

*Patient disposal*

Apart from deciding whether to treat a patient's enquiry as emergency or routine, this means soothing patients who have, or think they have, a complaint, and knowing just when to refer the complaint to the optometrist or whether an optometric assistant can handle it (again, *see* Chapter 19).

*Maintaining the reception area*

This is the first room in the practice the patient sees; a patient's loyalty is often made or broken by first impressions. An effort should be made to keep a reasonable range of up-to-date magazines, as well as ensuring that the area is clean and tidy.

**Typing or word processing**

This includes preparing letters to patients, doctors and so on, producing reminders in slack periods and accounts at the end of the month.

**Routine office work**

*Invoices and statements*

Statements for materials supplied to the practice are checked against invoices, any discounts calculated and cheques written out in full except for the signature. This is added at a time convenient to the optometrist after a final check by him.

*Stock control*

A watch is kept over the levels of stock of those items sold at reception; for example, contact lens solutions, spectacle cases, chains, cleaning cloths and solutions, together with the reserves of the usual office stationery, appointment cards, reminder cards, spectacle/lenses ready cards, practice literature (*see* Chapter 19), stamps and NHS forms. New supplies are ordered in good time and a buffer stock kept elsewhere in case of emergencies.

*Book-keeping*

A record of each cash transaction is kept and analysed in a day book. At the end of the day this is reconciled with the cash in the till, making allowance for the float; any other income, such as NHS, HES or lecture fees received, is added and the total put in a safe or banked. A record of any petty expense is recorded in a petty cash book; this is best analysed and reconciled weekly. Statistics, without which it is impossible to run any business efficiently, are most easily collected as they are produced. A record of each patient seen, together with details of any dispensing, forms the basis of proper fee calculation. The receptionist is the best placed member of staff to maintain these statistics.

*Fees and charges*

The receptionist must be a mine of information for any patient's enquiry regarding fees, the cost of appliances, contact lens insurance, etc. In these cost-conscious, consumer-orientated days, prompt, accurate estimates must be forthcoming to any enquiry concerning charges. This means explaining, if necessary, why the charges are calculated on a cost of materials plus fee basis, which is, of course, the only system defensible on professional grounds of paying for one's time and expertise.

*Repairs*

The receptionist will be able to carry out simple repairs, such as replacing screws and sides, while the patient waits. More complicated jobs will be passed on to the dispensing assistant, or the workshop if you have one, or sent away to the prescription house.

## Optometric (dispensing) assistant

Of course the optometrist may wish to employ a dispensing optician and simply be responsible for the eye examination. However, if he prefers to retain complete accountability to his patient, including the dispensing if any, then he will favour a dispensing assistant. The duties may be outlined as follows.

### *Spectacle frames*

*Selection and suitability*

Many optometrists prefer to discuss the most suitable type of frame for the patient's prescription, occupation and recreations before he leaves the consulting room. For instance: thick frames with wide sides are not suitable for driving; deep frames are best for bifocals; thin rims will make deep minus lenses more obvious. It is very convenient to be able to pass the patient over to an assistant with the request that she demonstrate certain frame types to the patient while you continue with the next appointment. The more unusual appliances such as make-up spectacles, billiard spectacles and prescription swimming goggles can be discussed at leisure, using clip-in lenses if necessary to enable the patient to assess the cosmetic effect.

*Provisional measurements*

Besides advising the patient on the cosmetic effect of different frame designs and colours, the dispensing assistant can make a preliminary judgement on their suitability in relationship to the range of sizes available. As the assistant becomes more proficient at this task, a lot of the optometrist's professional time can be saved, leaving him to check the measurements and fitting before making a final decision on bifocal heights, centration of lenses, tints, toughening and so on.

*Dealing with frame representatives*

Dispensing assistants are much more cost effective at choosing frames for stock than optometrists. Given guidelines regarding price, materials, construction and range of measurements and colours, they can afford to spend more time discussing the fashion aspects of spectacle frames with representatives while the practitioner gets on with work only he is qualified to do. Even so a rule should be made that reps are seen only by appointment.

*Frame stock control*

If frames are used from stock, obviously supply levels must be watched carefully and replacements ordered. Some optometrists like to have in quantity two or three different styles of men's and ladies' frames which are made in a large range of sizes. In this way patients who require their spectacles urgently can be dispensed these and only the lenses have to be ordered.

### Spectacle lenses – selection and suitability

Just as the most suitable type of frame is best discussed by the time the patient has left the consulting room, so with the lenses. Throughout the examination the optometrist will have been gaining invaluable information concerning the lifestyle of his patient. For instance: whether he sits at a wide desk and is likely to require executive-type bifocals; whether he plays cards and would benefit from trifocals so he can see clearly the cards in the middle of the table; whether the patient uses clip-on tinted lenses a lot and would appreciate the convenience of photochromic lenses; whether the reduction in weight and extra safety of plastics lenses are worth considering bearing in mind their susceptibility to scratching. Even when the material and form of the lenses have been agreed, it is still worth asking your dispensing assistant to get out the relevant trays of demonstration lenses to actually show the patient the type of lens you have been discussing before taking final measurements and ordering. This can prevent misunderstandings later such as the patient feeling that the bifocal is too obvious or the tint the wrong colour after the job has been completed.

### Fee implementation

The assistant works out the fees and charges for the patient, whether they are NHS or private. This is, of course, much simplified if dispensing in the practice is run on the basis of cost of materials plus fee. If this is the case, the assistant looks up the cost of the lenses including prisms, tints, toughening, etc. in a current prescription house price list and adds your professional fee – which will include overheads, NHS subsidy and your dispensing fee.

### Ordering and checking of lenses and frames

The dispensing assistant will transfer the approved frame and lens details from the patient's record to the particular prescription house order pad. The prescription house chosen will depend on several factors. For example, if special lenses are needed or the lenses require surfacing, the job should be sent to a house with the necessary stock and facilities. Likewise, to prevent delays, the job should go to an optical company which has supplies of the required frame. On the other hand, most optometrists will have an arrangement with one or more prescription houses which will involve obtaining a level of discount depending on the volume of prescription work sent to them. In this case a careful watch must be kept to ensure that the discount is earned.

When the order has been posted off (or collected if the prescription house offers a collection and delivery service, or taken to your own workshop if you have such a facility), some form of check must be kept to spot delays as soon as they occur. It is essential public relations to keep patients informed of any hold-up before they feel it necessary to contact you. One method to accomplish this is to put colour-coded or day-of-the-week tags on records before they are filed in the 'on order' drawer. Another is to keep a diary in which the patient's name is written on the day the job is expected back. If the practice is computerised, the computer can be asked to produce a list of all outstanding orders at any given time. Whenever an overdue job is detected, it should be promptly chased (this is where a second, ex-directory telephone line is such an advantage) and the optometrist who carried out the examination informed so that he can telephone or write to the patient to warn him of the delay and give a new delivery date.

The assistant should be expected to check the completed spectacles within an hour or so of their delivery. In this way, rejected jobs can be sent back by return and the patient notified. Of course, the responsibility for this is not the assistant's: before any spectacles are actually returned, they are double checked by the optometrist. This ensures that the assistant is not expecting unreasonably high standards and also keeps the practitioner in touch with the quality of work from the various prescription houses with which he deals. In case the reader is sceptical of letting his assistant undertake the checking, it is invariably found that assistants treat the task very seriously, often detecting faults which the optometrist himself has difficulty in finding!

The assistant will also compare the price of the frame and lenses charged by the optical company and shown on their invoice against the cost of materials quoted to the patient for each job. If any discrepancy is found, the list of material costs used in the practice is immediately amended so that the next patient to be prescribed those frames or lenses pays the updated costs. This sort of task is totally non-cost-effective if performed by professionally qualified members of staff. Similarly, discontinued frames and lenses should be promptly removed from the practice lists. There is nothing more infuriating that spending a long time advising a patient about the most suitable appliance for his optical problems, only to discover a week later than the frame is no longer available. It does not usually impress the patient either.

Focimetry can also be carried out on a new patient's old spectacles while the optometrist is taking the history and symptoms, thereby freeing him to spend time on the more clinical aspects of his work.

### Fittings and adjustments

#### Provisional fittings

These may be accomplished by the dispensing assistant when the patient returns to collect his new spetacles. After referring to the record for the original measurements, the joints may be filed out, the sides angled, the bifocal heights checked, etc. if the prescription house has not already done this, and the spectacles provisionally fitted. Of course, the optometrist's final approval is sought before the patient leaves the practice with his new correction, when further minor adjustments may be necessary for the perfect fit. However, considerable professional time will have been saved as the major adjustments will have already been done. In some cases, for example fitting progressive power lenses, the practitioner will want to do the complete fitting himself and will have made a note to this effect on the record after checking the provisional measurements at the dispensing.

*Adjustments*

Assistants can cope with the majority of patients themselves when they call in for routine adjustments such as bringing in the sides after a year or two's wear. After all, it is better for optometrist and patient alike if the problem can be solved immediately without interrupting an eye examination or insisting that the patient return at some later date for an appointment with the prescriber. There is one exception and that is the visit amounting to a complaint. If the problem cannot be solved instantly, as in the case of a lost screw, then the optometrist should be involved because a patient could easily be lost (and others if the complaint is voiced elsewhere) if the situation is not satisfactorily resolved. In fact, it is vital that all complaints of whatever nature be brought to the notice of the optometrist in order that he can reorganise the practice to prevent them in future if possible. This is the essence of good practice management – to learn from your mistakes (*see also* Chapter 19).

### Dispensing and fitting room maintenance

The assistant will put away the files, screwdrivers, pliers, etc. following a fitting, and sample frames and lenses following a dispensing. It may be necessary to order a further selection of frames for the patient to inspect at a later date if your range does not include exactly what he had in mind. She will ensure that the stock of stationery available in the dispensing and fitting rooms, such as Department of Health and Social Security forms and receipt pads, is adequate and that the frame and lens catalogues are up to date both for ranges and for costs.

### Optometric (clinical) assistant

The use of clinical assistants is still novel to most British optometrists. However, their employment is the most important single step a practice can make in order to improve the lot of both the practitioner and the patient. A discussion now follows of the various functions which may safely be delegated to clinical assistants. It will become apparent that they can be employed to the maximum potential only if a separate clinical tests room and/or contact lens instruction room is available in the same way that a dispensing assistant functions best in a dispensing room.

### Consulting room (chairside) assistance

This is essentially remaining with the optometrist during the examination to record data, pass instruments and carry out procedures which the optometrist is prepared to delegate and has ensured that his assistant is trained to do. These might include measuring vision and pupillary distance and the instillation of eye drops.

Some practitioners teach their assistants to record the patient's history and symptoms before they see the optometrist. This is done either prior to entering the consulting room or before the optometrist arrives. some practitioners (including the author) have misgivings over this use of assistants, as they would argue it takes years of experience and a full academic optometric training to take symptoms and history efficiently. However, for those who would like to attempt to use assistants in this way, a form on which to record the patient's details is essential. This should be along the lines of that shown in *Figure 16.1*, the controversial section of the form being the 'reason for appointment'. It is suggested that an *aide*

```
NAME: ..............................................................  AGE: ...............

ADDRESS: ...............................................................................
         ...............................................................................

DOCTOR: ...............................................

OCCUPATION:    Type of work:.............................................................

               Industrial hazards: .......................................................

               Illumination: .............................................................

REASON FOR APPOINTMENT: ...............................................................
.......................................................................................

OCULAR HISTORY:    Personal: ...........................................................

                   Relatives: ...........................................................

GENERAL HEALTH: ...........................................................................

MEDICATION: ...............................................................................
```

*Figure 16.1* Form on which to record symptoms and history

*memoire* similar to that shown in *Figure 16.2* is used systematically on every occasion by the assistant, to help complete this section and record all relevant answers. The last two rather more mundane potential reasons for the appointment should not be overlooked in the search for clinical data as they probably are amongst the most likely!

Other responsibilities in the consulting room consist of routine maintenance such as the cleaning and upkeep of instruments, cleaning the trial case lenses and frame, replacing the paper chin-rests on the slit-lamp, and so on. 'Disposables' also need replacing and an eye kept on their stock levels. These include batteries, bulbs, contact lens solutions and accessories, medications, fluorescein, tissues, Bjerrum screen pads, etc.

REASON FOR APPOINTMENT (note which eye if applicable)

BLURRED VISION:      Distance, near or both

HEADACHES:      Family history:
                Onset and duration:
                Character and position:
                Severity:
                Associated symptoms:
                Effect on vision:

OCULAR INFLAMMATION:   Pain
                       Infection
                       Discharge
                       Effect on vision

LOSS OF VISION:      Position in field

DIPLOPIA:      Horizontal or vertical
               Monocular or binocular

DISTORTED VISION:   Photopsiae
                    Floaters
                    Shadows
                    Coloured haloes

SPECTACLES OR CONTACT LENSES LOST OR BROKEN

WANT SPARE SPECTACLES OR CONTACT LENSES

*Figure 16.2* 'Reason for appointment' *aide memoire*

## Additional clinical tests

To delegate the task of performing additional clinical tests to a clinical assistant efficiently requires a clinical tests room. In there, the well trained assistant can undertake many tests and procedures for which the hard pressed optometrist would either have to re-book the patient to complete or simply miss out. These procedures include the following.

### Measurement of visual fields

The use of visual field screeners which require no interpretation of results are the least questionable; for example, the Friedmann Visual Field Analyser or Fincham–Sutcliffe for central fields, and one of the computerised bowl-type perimeters such as the Ocuplot or Fieldmaster for peripheral fields. Amsler charts and the Friedmann macular function and dark adaptation tests may also be employed by well trained assistants. However, most optometrists would agree that examination by Bjerrum screen and arc perimeter should be carried out only by themselves as they require interpretation.

### Measurement of intraocular pressure

The non-contact tonometer (NCT) is a major blessing as far as the busy practitioner using clinical assistants is concerned. Again, it is a screening instrument, with no interpretation of the results required. Assistants become extremely efficient with the NCT after a short time. Since the more conventional tonometers require the instillation of anaesthetics and a professional judgement of the readings obtained, most optometrists would not delegate their use.

*Note*   The author never refers a potential glaucoma case on the basis of the results obtained by assistants using visual field and tonometric screening instruments, for two reasons: first, it is not in anybody's interests to refer unnecessarily and the comparison of results taken from several different instruments gives a certain sense of security; secondly, most hospitals are more familiar with measurements taken on the Bjerrum screen and Goldmann tonometer. For the latter reason it is suggested that screeners be used only to arouse suspicion and monitor results over a period of time; the optometrist confirms the diagnosis or otherwise uses the Bjerrum and Goldmann (in combination with the ophthalmoscopic findings) before referral.

## Colour vision evaluations

Assistants readily learn to screen patients accurately with pseudoisochromatic plates, provided that the usual precautions regarding working distance and illumination are emphasised. Measurements by assistants with the various colour lanterns are possible, too, since no interpretation is required, only data collection.

## Sphygmomanometry

The measurement of blood pressure in optometric practices is becoming increasingly common. However, with the introduction of electronic sphygmomanometers, requiring no professional judgement of end-point but simply a recording of the digital readout, the delegation of this test is an obvious one.

## Tears tests

Estimation of the tear supply by Schirmer test strips can be carried out by a clinical assistant as long as the usual precautions are taken for an accurate result. The assistant can carry out with equal efficiency the simple test for nasolacrimal duct patency by instilling fluorescein and then inspecting a tissue (into which the patient has blown his nose) with a Burton lamp. Tear film break-up time (BUT) could also be delegated provided, of course, a slit-lamp is accessible to the assistant.

## Orthoptics

Routine procedures such as checking progress by the measurement of vision and visual acuity, the application and removal of occluders, teaching the patient exercises to do at home and the use of various pieces of apparatus are easily undertaken by clinical assistants.

## Contact lens assistance

### History taking

The clinical assistant helps the potential contact lens patient fill in a standard questionnaire (as in *Figure 16.3*) before he is seen by the optometrist. This is

NAME: ..........................    ADDRESS: .........................................

..................................................................................................

DATE OF BIRTH: ......................    PHONE NO.:   Home: ...........................
                                                      Work: ...........................

OCCUPATION: ...........................    HOBBIES: ...........................................

DOCTOR: .....................................    GENERAL HEALTH: ...........................

CURRENT MEDICATION (incl. birth control pill): ...........................................

..................................................................................................

MOTIVATION FOR CONTACT LENSES:   Cosmetic / Sport / Medical

DO YOU HAVE, OR HAVE YOU HAD, ANY OF THE FOLLOWING:

|  | No | Yes | At present? |
|---|---|---|---|

Eye disease or eye surgery:
(if yes, please describe)

..................................................................................................

Allergies, incl. hayfever:
(if yes, to what?)

..................................................................................................

Sinusitis:
..................................................................................................

Catarrh:
..................................................................................................

Skin disorder:
(if yes, please specify)

..................................................................................................

Dandruff:
..................................................................................................

Watery or dry eyes:
(if yes, please specify)

..................................................................................................

Menopause:

*Figure 16.3* Questionnaire for contact lens fitting

far less controversial than the assistant filling in the routine eye examination questionnaire (*see Figures 16.1 and 16.2*) since the same standard questions are always asked prior to a contact lens fitting.

## Fitting assistance

A great deal of time may be saved even if the clinical assistant is employed only as a scribe and simply writes readings and comments down on the record as they are called out by the optometrist. However, if the practitioner and his assistant work together as a team, rather like a surgeon and theatre staff or a dentist and nurse, the greatest benefits will accrue. As the working relationship develops between optometrist and assistant, the latter will know just when a tissue or fluorescein strip is required, without even being asked. She will know where each fitting set or stock lens is kept and retrieve it while the optometrist carries on with the examination. Some practitioners expect their assistants to take keratometry readings, palpebral aperture size and iris and pupil diameters. This is obviously best done before the optometrist appears, or he will be doing the assisting!

### Dispensing contact lenses (instruction)

The assistant is responsible for teaching the patient handling, wearing times and the care of the eyes and contact lenses before they are taken away from the practice. Needless to say, all verbal instructions must be confirmed in writing, preferably in the form of in-house produced or proprietary booklets which become the patient's property.

It should be stated that, as a general rule, dispensing should not be delegated unless it is certain that the optometrist who fitted the patient or a colleague will be on the premises should any queries arise. The assistant must not allow the patient to leave with the lenses if there is any doubt whether the patient can handle them or whether he will comply with the advice on the wearing of or caring for the lenses.

The teaching may be done on a one-to-one or two-to-one or more basis, as has already been discussed in Chapter 15 under 'Contact lens instruction room'. However, the wishes of both the patient and the assistant must be taken into consideration, together with the logistics of teaching several patients with different lens materials and care systems at the same time. Obviously a higher ratio of patient to teacher becomes more feasible in a large contact lens practice, where patients being fitted with similar materials may be grouped together more easily. It makes sense to ensure that the same clinical assistant, present at the fitting of the lenses to a certain patient, does the instruction for that patient. In this way, any unusual or special features associated with the particular lenses or care systems dispensed can be discussed with all those involved.

Most clinical assistants enjoy dispensing contact lenses more than any other part of their job because no two patients and their lenses are alike, and there is a great sense of satisfaction to be gained from teaching patients completely new skills from scratch and helping to solve individual problems. There is also the feeling that one is involved in a highly technological and rapidly developing science for which one must keep up to date on the latest materials and lens designs in order to dispense contact lenses competently.

Apart from discussing with the patient the usual problems associated with adapting to contact lenses for the first time, such as flare in dim illumination with hard lenses and the potential difficulties of wearing soft lenses in a dry atmosphere, the assistant must appreciate and understand why, for the purposes of dispensing, patients fall into one or more of the following groups according to their visual disability, and certain topics must therefore be emphasised more than others.

1. Myopes. Generally these are the easiest group to instruct because, unless the myopia is combined with high astigmatism, they can at least see the

contact lens clearly on the end of their finger. Occasionally, if the myopic error in the non-dominant eye is suitable (say, between −1.00 and −2.50) and the patient is presbyopic, then only the short-sighted dominant eye will be corrected. The patient may well initially be more aware of the lens due to the thicker periphery of a minus lens. He may also have initial difficulties if he usually removes his spectacles for near vision due to the different accommodation/convergence relationship between the eyes. Objects will appear closer than the patient is used to when wearing spectacles.

2. Hyperopes. Difficulties associated with poor vision, distance and near, may be remedied with certain magnifying mirrors and/or monocular flip-up spectacles. Objects will appear further away than the patient is used to when wearing spectacles and so special care should be taken when driving; for example, the gate post will be closer than it seems!

3. Astigmats. Again, there are problems with both distance and near vision in high astigmatism without correction, but also more lid awareness in eyes with regular astigmatism fitted with rigid lenses and spherical back curves. In eyes with irregular or oblique astigmatism, there is more chance of the lens decentring in the first few days of wear.

4. Presbyopes. If the patient is to be dispensed contact lenses for distance correction then the assistant will ensure that the patient does not take the contact lenses away without the reading spectacles, usually in the form of half-eyes, which will have been prescribed by the optometrist at the original fitting. If the correction is to be by monovision, the early difficulties to be expected, which will have already been discussed by the optometrist with the patient, will be reinforced by the assistant. These will include slight problems in judging distances and a feeling of being 'off balance'. If the patient has expressed a desire for occasionally having the best possible binocular vision when, for example, he represents his county in tennis tournaments, he may be dispensed three lenses, one of which will be to correct his distance vision in the eye that usually wears the near vision lens. The most sophisticated way to correct presbyopia with contact lenses is with bifocals, in which case the clinical assistant will emphasise the likely difficulties in the same way as the dispensing assistant would describe those with bifocal spectacles.

5. Aphakes. The main problem here, apart from extreme hyperopia, is that in the case of an elderly person there is sometimes a concurrent systemic problem such as arthritis which precludes the patient handling the lenses himself. In these cases, the assistant will be instructing the spouse or relative or friend on the handling and care of the lenses. In the case of an infant, the parents will receive the tuition.

6. Special. This group includes cosmetic lenses, scleral lenses and bandage lenses. Space precludes discussion in greater detail of the problems peculiar to special lenses, but the assistant must be fully aware of rules such as not using a bleaching regimen with hand-painted cosmetic soft lenses!

Finally, before the patient leaves the practice with the lenses, the assistant must first ensure that the patient makes another appointment at an appropriate interval (it is good public relations and may allay unfounded fears if an outline of what is likely to take place at that next visit is given as well). Secondly, the patient must be given a card on which is printed the telephone number of the practice and the home numbers of the optometrist who fitted him and any professional colleagues working in the practice. This is in addition to the home numbers being recorded on a 24-hour telephone answering machine for use in emergencies, and gives the patient a great sense of security. The number of telephone calls received in this way is, to a large extent, a good test of the expertise and communication ability of both the optometrist and his assistant.

*Contact lens aftercare visits*

This follows on from fitting assistance discussed above. Again the assistant can be extremely helpful even if used only to write down findings and measurements, although most assistants soon realise that aftercare visits usually follow a set routine and will know when to hand fluorescein strips, tissues, etc. to the practitioner. Some optometrists, notably in the USA, expect their assistant to carry out almost a full aftercare before they see the patient. In this way, everything except perhaps slit-lamp biomicroscopy and the assessment of lens fit is completed before the optometrist enters the consulting room, leaving him with just these tasks and the evaluation of any problems elicited by his assistant, followed by advice for their eradication.

# 17

# Recruitment and training of receptionists, optometric assistants and other non-professional staff

**Recruitment**

There are three occasions when it is necessary to recruit a new non-professional member of staff.
1. When a practice is being started from scratch.
2. When a practice has expanded and more assistance is required.
3. When a member of staff is leaving.

If the last is the case and there is no obvious reason such as pregnancy or moving away from the area then it is worth determining the exact cause. If not, the problem may well occur again with all the disruption it can produce, as in mending a fuse before discovering why it blew in the first place. Perhaps the most common, avoidable, reason for leaving is the feeling of being taken for granted. This is bad management. It is the optometrist's fault, as it shows he has not been aware of his staff's feelings and morale. Not only should occasional full staff meetings be held to iron out general niggles and policy, but it is essential that the optometrist make time to talk to each member of staff in private from time to time to ensure that any potential, difficulties are nipped in the bud. The optometrist has a duty to his staff to be sympathetic to their problems and positive in their solutions. Simple actions such as realising when a person is going on holiday before pay day and remembering to pay her in advance before she goes, without her having to come and ask you, shows you care about her feelings. If an assistant stays late, because you have seen an emergency appointment or the money does not balance, it is thoughtful to offer to take her home in case she has missed the last bus. No optometric practice, or any group of people for that matter, can work at its full potential and maximum efficiency unless its members enjoy mutual respect and are working together for the common good.

How does one go about finding a new member of staff? Before this question is answered, it is necessary to give some thought to the qualities being sought and just what is being offered, as this will have a direct bearing on where to look. Some points for consideration are as follows.

*Age*

If a completely new practice is being started, with, initially, only one optometric receptionist/assistant to help the optometrist, it may be wise to employ an older woman who does not intend to have children or whose children have left school, or she will be compromised if her children are ill or on school holiday. It is even better if she is established in the local community with little chance of having to leave the area due to family commitments. This is to endeavour to establish some permanency in the post. After all, the optometrist is going to have to teach those activities peculiar to an optometric office and practice himself (unless the applicant has been recruited from a similar position). It would therefore be most frustrating if a fully trained assistant were to leave before the practice had expanded enough to have taken on another and trained her to a similar level of efficiency. In the latter case, the colleague could have played a major part in the training of the replacement.

In a practice where there is already a stable, mature assistant, it may be sensible to consider a younger candidate, especially if she is to be trained to take on the role of a clinical assistant. There is the additional advantage that the practice will be more appealing to all age groups of patients if the members of staff are similarly varied.

### Qualifications

Again, depending on whether the post is a new one, an additional one or for a replacement, different qualifications will be desirable. For example, a solitary assistant who is to be a Jack-of-all-trades must have a good grounding in general office management such as typing, book-keeping and so on before she arrives, leaving the optometrist to teach her more specialist optometric skills. These will not be so important if the position is an additional one, for if the candidate shows promise, she can always be released for college training in general office duties whilst learning dispensing and clinical procedures from her fellow assistant(s) when in the practice.

### Salary

Some thought should be given to what salary the practice can afford. This may be interrelated with both age and qualifications discussed above.

The author does not believe in a salary scale strictly related to age and/or years of service. As far as remuneration is concerned, the candidate is told the starting salary, and that, as she becomes more proficient, rises will be given until she is as versatile as the other assistants, when she will earn the same wages, regardless of age or length of service. This may take a year or longer. It is possible she may never become completely interchangeable with her colleagues although this has never happened in the author's experience.

### Selection

The most obvious method of attracting new unregistered staff is via an advertisement in the local newspaper, but local conditions may make alternative routes worth considering. For example, the professional journals carry classified advertisements both for and by 'receptionists', although these are usually for vacancies in the big cities. Some optometrists may see an advantage in recruiting an 'experienced' person – someone who has been trained at the expense of another practitioner's time and money – but they must expect to carry out a certain amount of retraining as it is most unlikely that their previous employer had the same ideas about delegation and style of management as the new employer. If the candidate has been used to years of simply making appointments, answering the telephone and occasionally pricing up NHS forms, the delegation of contact lens instruction and sphygmomanometry may prove too much. Many optometrists will therefore prefer to offer the post to someone who is completely new to optometry and has no preconceived ideas about the way in which a practice is run.

Another avenue which may be worth exploring is the local careers office or employment bureaux. Care must be taken, however, that they are acquainted with the exact nature of the job and all the responsibilities it is likely to entail, since these agencies tend to greatly underestimate the scope of the job. On the other hand, if the optometrist has a contact or patient there, an enquiry could prove fruitful.

If a school leaver is contemplated, a telephone call to the local head teachers and careers advisors may be worthwile, especially during the months March to June when likely candidates will be considering their future.

Finally, personal recommendations may be sought from family, friends, patients, the other members of staff or the 'service' organisations such as Rotary. Of course the difficulty here is the embarrassment which may be caused if the newcomer proves unsuitable. At worst, not only will the selection procedure have to be repeated but also, unless handled delicately, another member of staff may leave as well if the candidate was her friend or a family of patients may be lost if she was related to them.

## The advertisement

Assuming that the time-honoured notice is to be placed in the local newspaper, what should it contain? If simply a request for a receptionist is made, potential applicants may assume that the job consists only of looking pretty and making appointments all day. On the other hand, the author once advertised for an optometric nurse and had five state-registered nurses amongst those to interview. Defining a job which most people have never even heard of is very difficult to achieve in a few words. It is best to leave the details until the interviews and insert an advertisement which, it is hoped, will attract a number of replies from which a suitable candidate may be chosen. An example would be:

# Optometric receptionist/assistant

Local Opthalmic Optician/Optometrist requires a person to train as an optometric receptionist/assistant. A background in clerical duties and typing would be an advantage but a willingness to help people is most important. Please apply, in own handwriting, giving details of qualifications and/or experience, to Box No. XXXX

Note the use of 'in own handwriting' and not just 'apply' or 'write' or 'telephone'. The neatness of the handwriting and the way in which a reply is set out can help as much in narrowing down the applicants for interview as the content of the letter. All relevant dealings with patients must be written on their record cards succinctly and legibly – there may even be legal implications – so that everybody in the practice is able to pick up the record and know immediately what the patient has been told and what action has been taken. Since a lot of your communication with the outside world is by letter, such as reports to colleagues, general practitioners, consultants and other professionals, each one is a reflection of your practice and so spelling is also important.

It is also best to use a box number. If addresses and telephone numbers are given, people will make direct contact at inconvenient times. It is plainly intolerable for a professional person with patients waiting to 'drop everything' and deal with casual enquiries about a vacancy.

When details of all the applicants (from whatever source) have been obtained, a list must be drawn up of those to be interviewed. If there has been a large response to the advertisement, say 50–60 letters, this is not easy. Do not put too much store in a long list of paper qualifications. As long as there appears to be a grounding in mathematics, science and English, and her letter is well presented, then the applicant is worth interviewing. Decide on the most promising half dozen and interview them as soon as possible. Do not write yet to those not selected for interview, in case a suitable candidate is not amongst the six and a further selection must be made. However, as soon as an assistant has been appointed, and even though those not interviewed do not know who the advertiser is, it is plainly only good manners to write to everybody who has shown an interest in the position.

### The interview

When the list of a half dozen potential candidates has been drawn up, there are two checks to be made before inviting the applicants to interview. First, look through your records. It is possible that one or more may be a patient of the practice. If this is so, useful information may be obtained about their general health, present employer, 'credit-worthiness', etc. Secondly, contacting present or former employers for an evaluation may be helpful (provided it is plain from the candidate's letter that she would be agreeable – if not, this must be left until permission has been obtained).

Ideally, it is best to set aside a morning or afternoon when the practice is working normally for the interviews, although this will naturally depend on its size. A limited assessment may then be made of the applicant's reaction to real patients, but, more importantly, the applicant will have a chance to get an idea of the 'feel' of the practice, something which is impossible when the practice is closed. The candidates should be contacted, preferably by telephone so that their telephone manner can be assessed, and appointments made at half-hour intervals.

Unless you are starting from scratch and looking for your first optometric receptionist, each candidate, before she meets you, should be shown round first by another assistant who has demonstrated an ability to judge people's characters and who will be present during the interview. This serves several purposes. From the candidates' point of view it relieves some of their nervousness as they are not immediately thrown in at the deep end with the person who is going to decide their fate, and it allows them to be shown the premises and equipment which they may be expected to use. They may also be more open about their hopes and aspirations with a potential fellow assistant or assistant whom they have come to replace. From your point of view it allows you to ask questions later about the candidate's initial impressions of the practice, it gives you time to absorb the performance of the previous interviewee before seeing the next and it allows your assistant to make an informal assessment of the candidate.

After the tour of the practice, the interview is probably best carried out in the consulting room, as reference can then easily be made to equipment and procedures. Maximum effort should be made to put the prospective employee at ease. The interview should develop into an informal chat between the applicant, your assistant and you. After all, the job primarily involves communication and getting on with all sorts of people besides patients, such as other professionals and the rest of the staff! To this end, avoid the common mistake of doing all the talking; the technique is to ask leading questions to provoke the candidate to do most of the talking, during which time you are mentally noting her voice, accent, appearance and general manner. Having confirmed the essential details of name, address, phone number, age and qualifications, other personal details should be requested such as previous positions and the reasons for leaving. This last should be substantial; you do not want to employ someone who finds difficulty in settling in any job. Particulars of present pay and required period of notice should be recorded.

A discussion of hobbies is often rewarding. Extrovert interests such as team games, social work, drama groups, etc. are more promising than introvert ones such as stamp collecting, bird watching and reading. Again, the emphasis must be on selecting a person with a proven ability of teamwork, communication and willingness to help others. Apart from this, involvement in the community by any member of the staff is a good practice builder.

The general health must be noted. Excepting the inconvenience to you of absenteeism, the effect on the other staff of one member being persistently away is very unsettling, however unavoidable the cause. This leads to the question of smoking. Any health care profession should discourage smoking as a matter of principle. If you have such a policy in the practice, this must be made clear if the applicant is a smoker.

Perhaps one of the more delicate areas which must be explored at some point (particularly if the candidate is a woman!) is that related to marriage, having children, looking after present children, etc. A discussion on these topics can perhaps be introduced most easily by asking 'What are your present family commitments and responsibilities'. It is important to determine if a spouse's job may result in a move out of the area, in which case the assistant will leave and you will be interviewing again. If the candidate has children at school, what provisions are there for their care during school holidays or if they are ill?

An 'O' level in mathematics is not required, but it would plainly make life very difficult if the new assistant could not do the simple arithmetic involved in cashing up for the day and lens transposition. The correct answer to a question such as 'What does plus three minus five make?' should settle the problem.

Not that it will affect her being appointed, but a note of any holidays she has booked should be made or you may not be able to contact her when you make the final selection. It is also vital to ask if she is under consideration for any other position or has been granted any interviews elsewhere. There would be nothing more frustrating than to write, offering the job, only to be told she has accepted another.

At this point you may ask whom you may contact if you wish to seek references and they were not mentioned in her original letter.

If the answers and subsequent discussion on all the above points seem satisfactory and you feel that the candidate is a definite possibility, then it is time to inform her of the conditions of work. These include the hours she would be expected to attend the practice, the length of holidays, the rate of pay and how it may be expected to increase as her responsibilities and experience increase. It is probably a wise precaution to stipulate a three-month trial period on both sides in case the results of the interview prove misleading. If you pay for a uniform for your assistants, it should be provided after this period.

An outline of the training she can expect should be given (see later) and arrangements for day release discussed if she is lacking in the basic skills of office duties.

Finally, she should be asked point blank if she would accept the job if it were offered, so you know whether to keep her under consideration. After thanking her for attending and possibly offering to pay her expenses, she should be asked to contact you immediately if she has any further queries, but especially if she no longer wishes to be considered for the position. In turn, tell her that you will write to her within, say, two weeks to inform her whether she has been successful in her application.

After completion of all the interviews comes the time to compare notes with your assistant, remembering that it is probably more important that the successful candidate gets on with the other members of staff than with you. If the decision is not immediately obvious, other factors such as the distance those candidates under consideration live from the practice, availability of public transport and so on must be taken into account. If you feel that a second interview is necessary, there was something wrong with the way you ran the first one. You should elicit the mistake for the future.

When you have made your choice, it remains only for you to telephone her referees before formally offering her the position if these prove satisfactory. Should this involve contacting a former employer, it is worth asking outright if he would employ her again. This is likely to provide a more revealing answer than a general enquiry.

The Employment Protection (Consolidation) Act 1978 states that employees working 16 hours or more a week must be given a written contract of service within 13 weeks of the commencement of the employment (*see* Appendix 4 for a general-purpose example). It is probably just as well to include the main points of this contract in the letter offering the job, ending with the request that she reply in writing at the earliest opportunity, accepting the position as detailed in the letter, so that you can contact the unsuccessful candidates as soon as possible.

Writing to the unsuccessful applicants includes of course not only those who attended for interview but also all those who took the trouble to reply to the advertisement. As there are likely to be a large number of similar letters, this is where a computer with 'mailmerge' facilities can save your typist several days' work. Keep the letters short. A suitable letter to those interviewed could read:

```
Dear  ...,

      Thank you for attending the interview recently for the
position of optometric receptionist/assistant.
      It proved extremely difficult to choose the candidate
whom we felt would fill the vacancy best, as you were all so
good.  This letter is to inform you that the position is now
filled, but we hope it will not be very long before you find
a position to suit you.

                    Yours sincerely,
```

A letter to those not offered an interview should be along the lines:

```
Dear  ...,

      Thank you for applying for the position of optometric
receptionist/assistant advertised recently.
      We were inundated with replies, a number of which
matched our requirements more nearly than your own.  This
letter is to inform you that the vacancy is now filled, but
we wish you every success in finding a suitable position.

                    Yours sincerely,
```

## Training optometric receptionists/assistants

At the present time, training is usually done 'in-house' in the UK, although several institutions, local associations and contact lens manufacturers have held, or are in the process of setting up, courses. In the USA, the first school for optometric assistants opened in 1967 and there are now over 30 different institutions offering a one- or two-year course.

Nevertheless, there can be a lot to be said for training in-house. Dental surgeons often prefer to train their own dental nurses rather than take on college trained ones, because the techniques and instruments used in the training institutions are sometimes so different from their own that they have to retrain them anyway! Probably the best formula would be a basic grounding in non-contentious subjects, such as NHS regulations and form pricing, simple ocular anatomy, physiology and pathology, principles of tonometry, visual fields, sphygmomanometry, colour vision evaluation, tear formation and drainage, visual training, lens design, focimetry, frame materials and adjustments, at college. The individual optometrist or his other assistant(s) could then teach those aspects likely to be peculiar to the particular practice, such as taking measurements and visual training on the particular instruments available, book-keeping, making appointments, ordering, stocktaking and so on.

If you plan to train your own assistant, perhaps the greatest virtue is patience. You have spent a lot of time, money and effort in making the correct selection; do not waste it for the sake of a little understanding. Each individual has his/her own pace at which he learns most effectively. Exceed that, and he will be overwhelmed. Reduce it, and boredom and inefficiency will set in. The skill on the part of the optometrist comes in tailoring the training to the individual.

Many procedures such as filing, checking invoices and statements, making appointments, repairs, minor adjustments and stock control are best learnt as they arise. More sophisticated operations such as tonometry, visual field measurement and sphygmomanometry must be taught in a more formal way. It is not possible between patients or during the odd broken appointment. Training time must be set aside, preferably outside the normal practice hours. Well prepared and illustrated seminars should be held, with the emphasis on the student gaining plenty of practical experience in the use of diagnostic equipment on you and her colleagues before she is asked to use it on real patients. This must be supplemented by carrying out a full eye examination on the new assistant, explaining each procedure in detail, and observing a variety of eye examinations conducted by you. These should include examples of the following patients: child, middle-aged, elderly, illiterate, non-English speaking; and should be followed by short discussions afterwards. In this way the assistant will understand what goes on in the consulting room – especially important if she is to become a chairside assistant – and will be able to take a more informed part in the running of the practice.

Only when you have built up enough confidence and trust in your new employee to do a procedure safely, accurately and without direct supervision should you consider its delegation. Even then, as she becomes more confident and experienced you must continually quietly monitor her efficiency at that procedure to ensure that the same high standard is kept. Naturally any criticism or suggestion you may have must be out of earshot of the patient. It must be regularly emphasised that education is a continuing process, for you as well as your staff, and this is why you observe them from time to time in order to ensure that the patient benefits from current thoughts and techniques described in the literature and meetings you attend. At the same time, for the practice to progress, you must constantly revise your opinion of whether other procedures could safely be taught to that assistant and delegated.

To add more interest to the training, the student could be sent to a frame manufacturer, prescription house and contact lens laboratory. Again, this will build up her confidence and efficiency in communicating with patients and dealing with their enquiries as she will be able to speak from first-hand experience. This in turn will boost the reputation of the practice, as so many 'service' industries are gaining the reputation of becoming less helpful and more indifferent to the needs of the consumer. As she progresses further, you may wish her to attend the increasing number of short courses, aimed at ancillary staff, being offered by various organisations. She can then report back to the next staff meeting, when everyone can benefit from the increased sense of unity and understanding which discussion brings.

Regarding staff meetings, these should be an integral part of the running of the practice. They must not take place for their own sake – everybody's time is too important – but whenever an agenda worthy of group discussion can be drawn up, a meeting should be called. This may be once a month or twice a year but everyone's opinion must be sought before any decisions are made. It is amazing how much the practice can benefit from the mutual respect and understanding which these meetings engender. They should not take place when the practice is open and there are likely to be interruptions. Either lunch-time or early evening is best, possibly taking the staff for a meal in a suitable local restaurant which will give them some compensation for the overtime involved. Keep the meetings well organised and the discussions to the point. Put the decisions into operation as soon as practicable so that everybody feels their contributions have been useful and that you show positive leadership.

A staff outing to one of the annual optometric trade exhibitions, perhaps combined with a visit to the theatre, would be another way of nurturing staff involvement and comradeship. As far as staff relations is concerned, it is worth repeating here that, as far as possible, you must always make yourself available to your staff if they have a problem, personal or otherwise, which they wish to discuss with you. A sympathetic ear and unbiased advice at the right time will prevent problems later.

Selected articles from the journals should be circulated amongst the staff to help in their continuing education, and textbooks made available for reference. *The Ophthalmic Assistant* by Stein and Slatt (1983), although primarily aimed at the ophthalmological aide, is a very useful book in this regard.

Finally, in striving to produce the best educated and most conscientious optometric receptionist/assistant in the country, it must be remembered that, although no doubt you will have instilled in her a burning loyalty to the practice and its patients, she is primarily working for money. Ensure, by making local enquiries, that you are paying her at least a reasonable rate for the job and review her salary regularly as she develops more skills and takes on more responsibilities. In the same way, pay for any time and expenses incurred by your staff attending meetings out of practice hours. If you have selected the right person and treat her as outlined above, you will be rewarded by an assistant with a fierce devotion to you and the practice.

## Other non-professional staff

### Prescription house staff

As mentioned in Chapter 15, when considering the workshop area, it may be necessary to employ two experienced glazers if it is intended to do all the prescription work in-house, to allow for illness and holidays. It therefore follows that at least one of them must be an 'all-rounder'. This means that he can do everything from metal and Supra glazing, to frame making and repairs. Such a person is difficult to find. The preferred method is to place a classified advertisement in *The Optician*. The other method is to approach a suitably experienced person and offer him a suitable inducement, whether this be purely financial or the freedom to run his own prescription house. It is probably best to delay equipping the workshop until you have found such an all-rounder in order to obtain his advice before buying. Having engaged him, if he is willing to teach his skills to another, it may be possible to find his understudy via the local newspaper or school careers advisors as when seeking optometric assistants.

Another approach would be to take on someone with proven practical ability and start with simple, single-vision glazing, sending out more complicated work until the recruit feels able to tackle that too. The Worshipful Company of Spectacle Makers regularly run courses for beginners as well as the more competent and it may prove wise to enrol your employees in one of these. Certainly with the advent of 'same day service' from the new optical shops appearing in the high street this whole area must be kept under constant review.

## Cleaner

The two important points to remember here are recommendation and references. Often cleaners work at several places. Unless the person is known personally to you, always conduct an informal interview. Show the candidate round the practice, explaining what responsibilities you would expect a cleaner to assume. If she is to clean before the practice opens in the morning, is she happy about turning off the burglar alarm, turning on the heating, and the like? If she is to clean in the evening, will you want her to turn on the burglar alarm, close the windows, ensure all your instruments are turned off, etc.? Is she just to dust and vacuum or do you intend her to wash the paint down (how often?), clean the windows, tidy up papers on desks, maintain her own stock of cleaning supplies (via the petty cash), replace blown light bulbs and so on?

After the tour, ask her if she cleans for anybody else and whether she would mind if you approach them for a testimonial. Obtain a couple of names of responsible people to whom you might apply for references. Be sure to follow these up. This particular employee, unlike any other, is going to be in your practice on her own. There may be cash lying about, and there will always be other, easily removed, items such as stamps, spectacle frames and pieces of office equipment. She will have all the necessary keys and could therefore enter at any time: weekends, holidays. Her character must be beyond reproach. Ensure that, if she is a smoker, she agrees never to smoke in the practice because of both the fire risk and the smell.

Engage her on a one-month trial basis. It will be obvious virtually immediately if she is able to do the job to your satisfaction. If she is, pay her well, including for holidays and illness. A good cleaner is harder to find than a good optometric assistant.

# 18

# Professional staff

This chapter includes the employment of both optometrists and dispensers.

## Optometrists

There are many reasons for wishing to share your patients with another optometrist. These may be short term, as in the case of holidays or illness, in which case the services of a locum may be in order. They may be medium term, which might make a pre-registration student suitable for a year. They may be long term, in which case locums and pre-registration students are joined by employees, associates and partners as possibilities.

### Locums

No less care should be exercised in the appointment of a locum than of a potential partner. He will represent your practice and, as far as the patients are concerned, is your equal. On a serious note, if a case of negligence arises from his action or omission, you may well be found equally and severally responsible for the remedy. So do not feel it is imperative to engage a locum at any cost just because you are to be away from the practice for a week or two. If you are worried by the lack of emergency cover while you are away, to cover contact lens problems for example, then a reciprocal arrangement with a local colleague could be the ideal solution, with you giving him similar cover when he goes on holiday.

On the other hand, you may know of a conscientious member of the local association who is perhaps trying to get a new practice of his own off the ground. In the early days, when he is establishing himself, he may welcome undertaking some locum work just as you may be very keen to offer it as a first step to expanding the practice enough to take on a full-time practitioner. You may be lucky and find a local female optometrist with a young family who could join you semi-permanently as a locum for ten years or so while her children are still at school. She will often be able to work flexible hours and be able to help you out during illness as well. This is what makes optometry such an attractive profession to those women who wish to combine their chosen career with raising a family.

If you have no personal local contacts but feel it is essential to seek a locum, as in the case of a lengthy illness, the Association of Optical Practitioners runs a national scheme as a service to its members to bring would-be locums and practices together.

As regards remuneration, some controversy exists as to whether the locum should be paid on a per case basis or per session (a morning or an afternoon). It is clearly more professional to work on the latter scheme, as is done with sessional optometric work in hospitals. An agreed patient load per session should be decided at the outset. In the case of a patient cancelling or failing to appear, the locum should not suffer financially. Equally, if an emergency patient appears, the locum would be expected to see him if he were free and not you. Again, the AOP will provide members with a current recommended sessional fee.

### Pre-registration students

A pre-registration optometry student is a university graduate who must be supervised for at least one year by an optometrist who has been registered with the General Optical Council for at least four years. After this year and on the successful completion of the Membership examination of the British College of Ophthalmic Opticians (Optometrists), he may apply to the GOC for inclusion on the Register. Many practitioners acknowledge their gratitude to the profession and try to repay their debt by taking on a pre-registration student every year. However, although the engagement of a student is a serious step and not to be undertaken lightly, this is not to say the benefits are entirely one-sided. The company of a new, up-to-date mind in the practice can be like a breath of fresh air, stimulating reappraisal of techniques and methods in the light of current thought and providing a deeply satisfying reward in the knowledge that you have helped lay the foundations of the student's aproach to optometry for the rest of his professional life. It would be dishonest to pretend that the year will be financially rewarding for the supervisor if undertaken conscientiously, but neither should it prove a drain on the accounts if organised properly.

As a first step, assuming you or a colleague working in the same practice has been registered for at least four years, contact the BCOO for a copy of their Guidelines for superivising optometrists and trainees. If you feel you can fulfil their criteria for approval as a pre-registration supervisor, you may apply for admission on their list. These criteria include:

1. The provision of comprehensive instrumentation for refraction, dispensing, visual fields, tonometry, colour vision testing and binocular vision evaluation.
2. The availability of all those drugs necessary for the practise of total optometric care.
3. The undertaking to provide the time and the finance to attend revision and tutorial courses.
4. The ability to offer a minimum of 500, to a maximum of 1200, eye examinations during the year.
5. An arrangement with an ophthalmic department of a hospital for the student to attend for the equivalent of 5–15 working days, primarily to

extend his experience in the recognition of abnormal ocular conditions. The College suggest that a token ex-gratia payment to the ophthalmic department of £200 for their help may be thought appropriate.

6. If the practice concerned cannot provide experience in the full range of optometric examination, for example in occupational visual welfare, then arrangements must be made for the relevant skills to be gained elsewhere.
7. Every help must be given in preparing the student for his professional qualifying examination, held towards the end of the year. This includes consultation on the preparation of 20 case records to be presented to the College prior to those examinations.
8. Only one supervisor may be responsible for one trainee unless a student has completed the year and is waiting to re-sit a failed section of the professional qualifying examination.
9. The supervisor must always be available to the trainee.

Provisional approval will be given upon the signing of an undertaking based on the above. Full approval will be given only after the delivery of a satisfactory report by a College Visitor to the College following inspection of the practice and an interview with the potential supervisor. This full approval lasts for three years. The inspection is not intended to resemble an inquisition, but to enable advice to be given on how both the supervisor and his potential trainee may make the best out of the year they will share. No ethical, conscientious optometrist has anything to fear from the visit.

On a financial note, recent years have seen the introduction of grants for pre-registration supervisors. Briefly, the maximum grant is for £1000 for the year, to be reduced by £1 for every £1 that the salary paid to the trainee exceeds the Whitley Council notional salary for trainee optometrists employed in the hospital eye service. Claims for grants should be made via the Family Practitioner Committee (England and Wales), the Joint Ophthalmic Committee (Scotland) or the Area Board (Northern Ireland).

If you gain the College's approval and decide to plough back some of your expertise and experience into the profession by taking a graduate under your wing for a year, do not forget that you are ultimately responsible to both your patients and your new charge; to the patient for any mistake or omission on the part of the trainee, and to the trainee for giving him the best possible introduction to real-life total optometric care. For this reason it is imperative that you discuss and check every single patient the trainee examines. At first this may mean repeating virtually everything. Towards the end of the year an ophthalmoscopy may be all that is required in many cases. If you are to undertake this obligation properly, you will have to be prepared to reduce your own patient load by about one-third to one-half when the trainee first joins you.

Finally, it should be made clear to the student in writing that he is being taken on for an initial period of the pre-registration year. Of course, this is not to say that the contract will not be renewed or even a partnership offered if it is mutually agreeable. However, it gives the employer some protection if the student proves entirely unsuitable by being unable, for example, to pass his final examinations, or if the supervisor finds he just does not have enough patients to go round at the end of the year.

### Employees, associates and partners

This is the category of interest if you are looking for a permanent, full-time, registered colleague. There is some confusion, however, over the distinction between the title 'employee' and 'associate', which is further blurred by the use of the words 'consultant' and 'assistant'.

'Consultant' is the name usually given to an optometrist who undertakes eye examinations only, possibly working on the premises of a dispenser, and therefore does not concern us here. The word 'assistant' implies inferior ability and/or degree of responsibility to the principal and is therefore to be deprecated, especially as it is likely to become confused more and more with the 'optometric' or 'clinical' assistant.

Many optometrists feel that the difference between an associate and an employee lies in whether they are paid on a self-employed basis or pay-as-you-earn. Of course, there can be tax advantages to being self-employed within a practice, for instance as regards pensions, apart from a feeling of greater independence. Unfortunately, in cases recently brought before the courts, it has often been held that, despite the title of associate, the practitioner is really no more than an employee unless it can be shown that he does not work mainly for any one firm. It is therefore prudent to avoid embarrassment later by seeking advice, before taking on any professional colleague (other than as a partner), regarding his eligibility for self-employed status. On the other hand, the considerable protection which the law gives to employees compared with the self-employed should not be overlooked.

### Recruiting optometrists

Your approach to appointing a colleague to work with you in your practice will depend to some extent on which of the above categories he fits. It is worth re-emphasising, however, that whichever it is, the public, and even the law, will probably look upon him as your equal in expertise and responsibility. It therefore follows that the greatest care should be exercised in selecting a colleague to work alongside you. You may well be choosing someone with whom you will be sharing the rest of your working life. Your choice could lead to a professional life full of satisfaction and comradeship or to one of frustration and regret.

A major point to consider, therefore, when selecting an optometric associate, is personal compatibility. Your new colleague should, as far as possible, have the same professional, social and financial aspirations as you. There are nearly as many shades of opinion on how the profession of optometry should be run as there are optometrists. Be sure that yours are as close as possible. Take plenty of time, especially if the appointment is designed to lead to partnership. The latter is in many ways like a marriage, only more so. The old saying, 'marry in haste, repent at leisure' is very pertinent. Consider the following.

### Age and sex

There will naturally be little choice regarding age as far as pre-registration students are concerned. If you are selecting a permanent locum for a session or more a week, it may be wise to pick a colleague in a completely different age group to yours. This is in order to give the patients more choice: some may relate better to an older practitioner, others to a younger. In the same vein, deliberately choosing a member of the opposite sex may attract more patients to the practice.

If a full-time, permanent employee is under consideration, there is always the possibility that this may ultimately lead to partnership and/or succession and so age and sex become of vital importance. Female (or single parent) candidates for partnership would want to ensure that arrangements could be made to provide continuity of patient care in the event of their becoming pregnant and/or to discharge their responsibilities to their children when they are on holiday from school or ill. This is not particularly difficult but many potentially excellent partnerships have not come to fruition because of unfounded reservations on the part of the male. What is important, as in any partnership, is to discuss all likely eventualities and their sensible management before signing the partnership agreement. As regards age, a difference of about five to eight years is probably ideal if partnership is contemplated, as this will provide the best continuity within the practice. The idea is that about once every five years one partner retires and another is taken on. In this, possibly idyllic, arrangement the firm would consist, at any given time, of an older partner, with a younger partner and an associate/employee in the wings both ready to 'move up' when the older optometrist retires. The author has intentionally avoided the use of 'senior' and 'junior' partners as this implies superiority in some way of one above the other. In a true partnership all partners are equal.

If early succession in a non-expandable one-practitioner practice is planned, then the age gap probably needs to be as wide as possible for continuity of care to the patients and cost effectiveness to the practice. If the practice cannot support two optometrists, the person retiring should do so as soon as possible, leaving the newcomer a long professional life of sole proprietorship.

## Qualifications

Paper qualifications, whilst important, can be misleading. The efficient practise of independent optometry requires great practical skill, both clinical and in the ability to relate to people whether they are working within the practice or coming to the practice as patients. The evaluation of these less tangible qualities is yours alone, based on a thorough interview and 'homework' (*see* later). However, qualifications, in addition to a first degree in optometry and membership of the College, such as a DCLP, MSc or FBCO by examination, probably indicate a greater commitment to the profession as a vocation, as well as a deeper clinical understanding.

## Salary

Mention has been made above of the help which the AOP is able to give as regards scales of remuneration for pre-registration students and locums. The Association is also willing to provide suggested salary levels for full-time employees related to their length of service with the firm and any managerial responsibilities they may assume. These figures, together with those gained from advertisements in the journals and other colleagues, will give a basis on which to set a reasonable starting salary in any given case. Whatever you decide this to be, it must be kept under constant review as your colleague assumes greater responsibilities.

### Selection

The obvious place to begin the search for potential candidates is via the classified columns of the journals. This has its disadvantages. Many advertisements are worded ambiguously, and with sparse detail, resulting in a lack of faith on the part of possible applicants. The 'family group' proclaimed often turns out to be a large multiple when the reply from the box number is received. Because of this, any advertisement should be very specific if it is to attract the sort of applicant you are seeking and not waste everybody's time and effort. For example:

## Young Optometrist

Young registered Optometrist required to join two colleagues with a view to eventual partnership. The independent practice is situated in south Devon and occupies a large Victorian house. It is run on the highest professional ideals with a large proportion of contact lens work together with sessions at the local infirmary. Box No. XXXX

## Optometrist

Registered Optometrist required for one session per week in Derbyshire city centre multiple practice. Eye examinations only and no contact lens work. AOP recommended sessional fee together with travelling expenses. Box No. XXXX

It may be said that an address should be given rather than a box number. However, the latter necessitates a letter in reply which can give useful information about the candidate before you even see him. If given the job, he will write to many people and each letter will be a reflection of the practice. Others might argue that in the new era of competition in the professions, it is not good business to advertise to the opposition in the same town that you are about to expand.

Other avenues for recruitment include the BCOO and the AOP, who maintain lists of different categories of possibilities such as pre-registration students and locums, as already mentioned.

A word in the ear of the secretary of the local AOP branch or local optical committee could be worthwhile. Occasionally, optometrists, especially pre-registration students, contact the nearest organisation, geographically speaking, to the part of the country in which they would like to live.

The London Refraction Hospital maintains a notice board for displaying vacancy advertisements, as do the optometric universities. A suitably worded card placed there may bring results.

### The interview

To avoid repetition here, the section in Chapter 17 concerned with interviewing potential optometric assistants should be read in conjunction with the present section.

You are likely to receive inquiries from anywhere in the British Isles, so, before inviting applicants for interview, it is well worth an initial telephone conversation with them. This gives you the opportunity to assess their telephone manner as well as to determine whether you are both talking on the same wavelength as regards methods of practice, patient load, prospects, salary and so on. In this way, nobody's time and money will be wasted by a completely unsuitable applicant travelling hundreds of miles. (It goes without saying that travelling expenses should be paid.)

If an agreement for further discussion is made, it is probably best to meet at the practice half an hour or so before it closes so that the candidate can see the place in action and meet the other staff. When everyone else has left, the more detailed tour of the practice and formal interview can take place, before the candidate is taken home or to the local restaurant for a meal. It is often very rewarding to invite the respective spouses to this dinner. Although it is not essential that everyone gets on with complete social harmony, a similar outlook on life is very encouraging, especially if the position is one with a view to partnership.

One of the most important items for discussion is why the candidate wants to leave his present position. It may be because he has been disillusioned with broken promises for the future. Increasingly it is because the practice where he fitted in so well has been taken over by a multinational concern, or by lay interests, whose only concern is maximum profit rather than patient well-being. He will want to make certain that you will stick to your ideals and that his future is more assured.

As when interviewing potential optometric assistants, you will need to record whether the candidate has any holidays booked in case you need to contact him. Again, general health and attitudes to smoking should be discussed, as should the position over any dependant relatives the applicant may have as regards illness and school holidays. A three-month trial period should be agreed.

If you feel at the end of the evening that the applicant is a strong contender for the vacancy, ask if he is at present considering any other jobs or has any other interviews to attend. Then ask him how interested he is in the position now he knows more about it. If he is very keen, ask him to contact you immediately if he changes his mind or has any queries. These precautions are to try to prevent the frustrating situation of offering him the job, only to find he has taken another or has changed his mind.

When you make your final choice, send a letter to the candidate offering him the position. When you have received his acceptance in writing, write to any others you may have interviewed, together with those applicants you did not meet. Specimen letters may be found in Chapter 17 in the section concerning interviewing potential optometric assistants. It would also be good manners to offer the new employee practical if not financial help with any removals and house hunting which may be necessary to enable him to join you.

## Dispensing opticians

Most of the foregoing advice pertains equally well to dispensing opticians except, of course, as regards partnership. Both the BCOO and the AOP have strong reservations concerning partnerships between optometrists and dispensing opticians. Indeed it is hardly fair to the dispenser to make him equally and severally responsible for the acts of his optometrist partner, as he would be in law, when the optometrist's sphere of activity is so much greater.

# 19

# Public relations and complaints

The theme for this chapter is 'honesty is the best policy' when it comes to communicating with the public at large and patients in particular.

## Communication with the patient

Once a patient has selected your practice for his eye care, the aim must obviously be to gain his confidence so that he never considers consulting any other optometrist, unless of course you refer him or he moves from the district. Indeed, a measure of the trust patients have in you is reflected in the number of requests you receive from former patients to recommend a colleague near to where they are moving. Although the technical side of optometric care is vitally important, unless you communicate what you are doing, what you have found, what your recommendations are and why, you will not impress your patients. The professions are often criticised for being aloof and reserved: perpetuate this impression at your peril.

### *Making appointments*

This is usually the responsibility of the optometric receptionist. Therefore ensure that throughout her training you emphasise how vital an area public relations is: her job depends on it as well as yours. When an appointment is requested, the patient should be asked:

1. Have you been here before?
2. Which optometrist would you like to see/do you usually see [if there are more than one]?
3. What time of the day and day of the week suits you best?

If a suitable appointment cannot be made soon enough with the optometrist of his choice, the patient should be asked if he would be prepared to see a partner or associate who is not booked so far ahead. If the patient shows concern at the length of time he must wait, it is essential to ask if there is some urgent reason for the appointment. Often an early booking will be sought because his spectacles have broken, in which case the receptionist and/or the dispensing assistant can handle the enquiry, possibly even by mending the spectacles on the spot or by making a temporary repair to keep the patient going until his appointment. If the patient is worried about a recent loss of sight or the health of his eyes, every attempt must be made for him to be seen that day, possibly immediately. This again underlines the considerable responsibility the optometric receptionist must assume in her job. Many a retinal detachment, acute glaucoma, retinal thrombosis or brain tumour has been successfully detected thanks to alert reception staff. It naturally makes things easier if the appointment book is drawn up to include spaces for 'emergencies'. All that is necessary is to leave one short appointment free every day. If it is not filled on the day then you can catch up with some administration and have a cup of coffee.

When a time has been agreed, the patient should be given a card to confirm the appointment and asked to bring any previous correction with him. Printed on the card should be a reminder to this effect and a note that if 24 hours' notice of cancellation is not given, or the appointment is broken, then a charge may be made. It is never cost effective to implement this threat, but it may help the patient to remember.

If a patient fails to appear for an appointment, the fact should be written on his record card for future reference. Ideally, the patient should then be contacted – for two reasons. First, as a service: he may have genuinely forgotten, in which case another time can be arranged. Secondly, he may just not have bothered to turn up, in which case you must find out why in order to see if there is a way to prevent a repetition with the same or another patient in future. For instance, the receptionist may have upset the patient in which case you may 'salvage' him (and possibly his whole family and friends) with an apology. At least you can take steps to stop it happening again. The easiest way to make this enquiry is by telephone. If this is impossible, a letter along the following lines will suffice:

```
Dear  ...,

     I note you were unable to keep your appointment with
me at  [time]  on  [date].
     Please contact us again to make further arrangements.

                    Yours sincerely,  ·
```

As most appointments are made and problems discussed by telephone, it is worth emphasising some points on telephone technique.

1. Answer as soon as possible – even if it means cutting short a conversation with another patient. Nothing seems more inefficient than a telephone left to ring and ring. It will be construed to reflect the tenor of the whole practice, especially if it is the first time that patient has contacted your firm. A further point: nothing is more frustrating than a line constantly engaged – another, ex-directory, line is essential for communicating with the prescription houses and for personal calls. If this is not possible, at least ask your staff to make or receive personal calls as little as possible – someone with a retinal detachment or someone who wants to know whom to make their cheque out to (!) may be trying to get through.

2. Identify the firm. For example: I. Seymour, Optometrists. Always use the firm's name, not 'this is the opticians', as it will tend to make callers identify themselves.
3. Speak clearly. For this reason, smoking, drinking and eating should be avoided on reception, apart from the unprofessional appearance these present to people waiting for attention.
4. Concentrate. Listen carefully and write down all the salient points; then if the patient makes an appointment or the call has to be passed on to a dispensing or clinical assistant, or optometrist, the patient does not have to repeat the whole story again.
5. Be concise and to the point. An efficiently handled call reflects an efficiently run organisation.
6. End the call politely and helpfully. It may have been long and difficult, with the person on the other end being abusive (unjustified, it is hoped!). If he is complaining, he should be assured that everything possible is being done and that he will be contacted again as soon as any more information is available or by a certain date. If an appointment has been made, it is useful to say, 'we'll see you on the [date] at [time] then'. This should sort out any misunderstandings which may have crept in during the conversation. To be doubly sure, some optometrists like to back up all appointments made by telephone by sending appointment cards as confirmation.

### Reception

Upon arrival for the appointment, the patient should be addressed by name (not 'sir' or 'madam') to make him feel welcome and expected. Treat him almost as if he were a visitor to one's own home by asking him if he wishes to remove his coat and, after getting him to sign any forms, etc., showing him where to sit 'until Mr [optometrist's name – not 'the optician'] is ready to see you'. If you are running late, this should be explained immediately, together with a realistic estimate of when you are likely to be able to see him, in case he feels he has time to run another errand before then.

When you are ready for him, either you should collect him personally, by name, from the waiting room, or another member of staff should bring him to you, unless it is someone frequently seen such as a patient being fitted with contact lenses. Again, the patient should be presented to you by name and, if you feel it is appropriate, shake hands with him to make him feel at ease.

### In the consulting room

Many of the public feel that the professions invent their own languages in order to impress or confuse and therefore justify higher fees. The author believes that the hallmark of a true professional is his preparedness and ability to progressively reduce the technical level of his communication with his client or patient until he is speaking on the same wavelength. It is true that 'the aetiology of asthenopia is related to non-compensated heterophoria at near' but so do 'poorly co-ordinated eye movements make your eyes ache when you read'. If you wish to use jargon, build up to it. For example, 'Well, Mr Jones, the window to your eye, or cornea, has a surface like a rugby ball or barrel. This is called astigmatism.' When you explain a problem, such as vitreous floaters, it is a good idea to reinforce the explanation with a printed leaflet so that the patient can read it at leisure and give an accurate account to his relatives or friends if necessary. These handouts can be obtained from organisations such as the AOP, but you may prefer to produce your own, using the phraseology which comes naturally to you (*see* later, 'Practice literature').

To gain the confidence of your patients you should ensure that they understand what you are doing and why you are doing it. How many times does one hear that a person is taking pills, but he does not know what they are called or what they are for. It is not his fault for not asking, it is that of the physician for not informing him. Every patient must leave your consulting room knowing more about his eyes and the optometric profession than when he came in. This is the best PR your practice can have: on a one-to-one, personal basis. In this way, any questions provoked by the information you give can be answered there and then in language tailored to the individual concerned. Media advertising can never accomplish anything like as much. What is more, the latter costs money and is likely to attract people for the wrong reasons (or the wrong people!) such as the cost of the frames. It is true that the personal approach to PR, made during an eye examination, is expensive in both time and patience, but it is the only way to build a practice of loyal patients who are unlikely to seek the advice of an establishment which offers 'Spectacles – 10% off all this week'. They must be attracted to the integrity of the practitioner and the service he provides, not by the cost of the pieces of plastics on his walls.

When you open the proceedings with 'What's brought you here today – are you having any problems with your vision?' you will often provoke many seemingly irrelevant details far removed from asthenopia. However, if it is mentioned, for example, that her eyes are tired because she has been up all night with their newborn infant, make a cryptic note on the record that they have just had a baby. Then, at the next visit, you can enquire after the child. This may sound insincere, but it is not: the fact that you have bothered to write it down shows your interest in the patient.

Do not be rude to the patient or reveal your irritation if he is indecisive during the examination. This sounds too obvious for words, but in every town there seems to be one practitioner who possesses an impossible chairside manner. For instance, he will show his annoyance when a patient has difficulty selecting the clearer image with the cross-cylinder or seeing the line in the Maddox rod test. If this happens to you, simply employ another technique to measure the same thing. It is a revelation of your incompetence rather than the patient's stupidity and certainly does not warrant the loss of a patient (and perhaps his family and friends) for the sake of a more relaxed and tolerant attitude. If patients seem to keep making the same 'mistakes' when answering your questions, then re-word them. If you feel that you will probably kill the next person who tells you that his vision has gone blurred when you put the +1.50s in for retinoscopy, ensure instead that you point this out to each and every patient as you take the lenses out of the trial case. In fact, the art in conducting an eye examination and dispensing, is to anticipate every potential problem before it arises. If you are prescribing a change of cylinder axis, say that the floor is likely to slope and walls will appear to be tilting when the patient first wears the spectacles. Estimate how long you would expect this to last until the patient adapts. With especially critical patients, such as those with a known sensitivity to different base curves, it will demonstrate your concern if you instruct them to make a short appointment a month after having their spectacles fitted, so that they can let you know how they are getting on. If you tell them the worst, they will be especially pleased with themselves if they have only a little difficulty, and they will not be back after few hours suggesting you have fitted them with someone else's prescription.

Students are often taught that they must not tell patients what they have found if it is pathological and/or they are to be referred. Except in extreme conditions, such as brain tumours, this author does not agree with this philosophy. If you spot a retinal haemorrhage and decide to refer for blood pressure and urine tests, tell the patient what you have found, what it probably signifies, why you are referring him to the doctor, what the doctor is likely to do and how any problem he detects is likely to be treated. If you do not, many will assume it's a brain tumour anyway. Even if you are not going to refer, as in early cataract, do not be afraid to tell the patient what they have, by name, and then proceed to explain it, preferably using a model eye and diagrams. Far from worrying them unnecessarily, they will be reassured, because you are then free to go on to explain why they experience difficulty from flare in sunlight (advise a peaked cap or a wide-brimmed hat) and why you are not changing their spectacles this time even though their vision is worse than last time. There is nothing worse than to find out that a patient has sought a second opinion and, after discovering the truth you withheld from him, has concluded that you are not capable of detecting a cataract – which is the real reason for his reduction in vision. Honesty is the best policy!

When you have been working flat out all day, have seen three emergencies and detected four glaucomas requiring five doctor's reports, you are likely to be a little behind with the appointments. Do not think, however, that your prowess with the ophthalmoscope means you do not have to apologise to each and every patient whom you keep waiting, with a brief explanation of why you are running late. Of course, your assistants will have kept them informed of the situation, but patients also may have other appointments to keep and you may have seriously inconvenienced them. Worse, they may have taken time off work, involving loss of earnings, only to sit frustrated in your waiting room for 40 minutes. When they do eventually find themselves in your consulting room chair, take special care not to give them the feeling you are rushing the examination – you must make them feel, even more than usual, that their eye examination was more thorough than ever before – and worth the parking ticket.

If you do find a significant prescription in someone who has never worn spectacles before, or a different prescription in a spectacle wearer, before you recommend a change of lenses, always try to demonstrate both the good and the bad effects which the new prescription will have. For example, if you have found than an extra +0.50 is required to make the patient see N5 comfortably again, put the old readers on his nose and, with the reading chart in place, put a pair of +0.50s over the top. Say: 'This is the change you will be paying for and you will be able to thread needles and see the numbers in the telephone directory clearly again. On the other hand, it will cost you

£XX if we just change the lenses, £XX if you have a new pair on the NHS and £XX if you have a private pair. Not only that, you will no longer be able to see things clearly at arm's length, such as in shop windows or recipes on a work surface in the kitchen. Do you think that the change is worth it to you? Patients' ideas of a cost effective change vary so much that it is well worth this precaution to ensure that you do not produce a patient with the complaint that they can see as well with their old spectacles as the ones you recommended, or that their new readers are no use as they cannot play the piano using them. This sort of precaution should be taken whenever altering prescriptions or prescribing spectacles for the first time.

Finally, even if you are unable to help a patient to see better with lenses, low vision aids or exercises, never say there is nothing else you can do to help, because there always is. For example, if he has been blinded or is amblyopic in one eye, discuss eye protection for the seeing eye when engaged in sport or DIY. If you cannot improve poor acuity in either eye, then a discussion of the advantages of inclusion in the Partial Sighted or Blind Registers (following referral to an ophthalmologist) would be in order, together with an introduction to the local social worker for the blind. Never, ever, let a patient leave with a feeling of no hope.

### In the dispensing room

If you have made a joint decision with the patient to prescribe – and, as explained above, except in the case of a young child it should always be joint – you introduce him to the optometric assistant, briefly discuss the recommended lens and frame designs and have him taken into the dispensing room (unless you are reglazing the patient's own frame, in which case you work out the fees in the consulting room and the patient leaves without even entering the dispensing room). Once in the dispensing room, the assistant will demonstrate suitable frames and the recommended lens design and, when a decision has been made, recall you for approval and final measurement. Of course the assistant will have explained the cost of the particular combination of frame, lenses, tint, case, etc. before you return, and it remains only for you to ensure a correct fit of the frame, record its size and

| TO PROFESSIONAL SERVICES | |
| --- | --- |
| Cost of right lens | £ |
| Cost of left lens | £ |
| Cost of frame | £ |
| Cost of case | £ ................................... |
| *Subtotal 1* | ................................... |
| VAT @ 15% | ................................... |
| *Subtotal 2* | ................................... |
| Professional fee | ................................... |
| *Total* | £ ................................... |

*Figure 19.1* Example of a private appliance account

take bifocal or multifocal heights if necessary. To prevent any confusion later, it is good practice for you to repeat the final total cost of the dispensed appliance and hand a written estimate to the patient as well. This will either be on an official NHS receipt if the spectacles are to be dispensed through the general ophthalmic services, or on a detailed statement such as in *Figure 19.1* if they are to be dispensed privately. It will be seen how simple it is to work out the total charge when this consists of the cost price of frames and lenses to the practice, straight out of the manufacturer's latest price list, together with a professional fee for the particular type of appliance. This professional fee consists of an overhead element, a health service subsidy and a dispensing fee related to the work and responsibility.

Needless to say, if the financial arrangements include help from the DHSS, this should be discussed discreetly out of earshot of anyone else, especially other patients.

Some optometrists feel that deposits should be requested before appliances are ordered. On the contrary, these should be avoided if possible, as they complicate the bookwork and suggest a lack of trust when the whole idea of public relations is to establish a foundation of confidence between practitioner and patient to encourage the latter to consult you for all his eye care in future. This applies equally to contact lens fitting: the patient should pay nothing until he is either wearing the lenses comfortably with no physiological problems for as long as they were designed to be worn, or the process of fitting has been discontinued for some reason, in which case only a proportion of the fees should be required.

### Collection of spectacles

If it is the first time that the particular patient has had spectacles, you should spend some time advising him how to use and look after them when he comes to have them fitted. Again this is an ideal time to reinforce your advice with a leaflet. Whether or not he has worn spectacles before, you should also repeat any difficulties you might expect him to have due to the prescription, and how long they may last. For example, the 'Jack-in-the-box' phenomenon with an aphakic correction or the 'no-man's-land' created at arm's length, when the bifocal reading add is +2.00 or more than the distance prescription.

When both you and the patient are happy with the fit of the spectacles, say something along the lines: 'Let me know if you have any problems. If they slip or hurt, come back straight away. If you have any difficulties actually seeing with them, try for about X weeks to see if the situation improves; if not, let me know.'

If you do not send out reminders, now is the time to ensure that there is a card in the spectacle case detailing when you recommend a re-examination. If this period is six months or less, it is worth making the appointment then. Finally, you pass the patient over to the receptionist for payment of the bill. In these days of inflation and cash-flow problems it is better not to encourage accounts.

### Telephone answering machine

To provide an impeccable service, your patients should be able to contact you 24 hours a day concerning their eye care. Generally this is rarely necessary or even worthwhile: a broken spectacle lens may be reported just as effectively on a Monday morning as on a Sunday afternoon. Nevertheless, a telephone answering machine does make it theoretically possible to offer advice round the clock as well as to enable patients to leave messages, cancel appointments, etc. at any hour convenient to them. If you are going to provide your home telephone number, and the author believes this should be accepted practice for every contact lens practitioner, if not all optometrists, then the message should run something like:

'This is I. Seymour, Optometrists. The practice is now closed but will re-open on [day] at [time]. If you have a problem which you feel is related to the health of your eyes, please ring Mr Seymour on [telephone number]. If you wish to leave a message, please do so. Be sure to leave your name, address and telephone number so that we can contact you if necessary. Please speak after the short tone.'

### Practice literature

Reference has already been made to practice literature. It is a vital part of patient communication, but should only be used to reinforce information and advice already given verbally to patients by the optometrist or the optometric assistant; it does not replace discussion. Booklets and leaflets may be obtained from several sources. Indeed the AOP use them as an integral part of their Practice Enhancement Programme. However, many optometrists prefer to produce their own individualised literature, as they can then stress those points which they feel are the most important and relate to their particular practice.

Many people are bemused by the eye examination, contact lens fitting, and explanations and advice concerning subjects about which they have had no previous knowledge. Although they seem to understand at the time, when they get home and try to recall the information either for themselves or for relatives or friends, they discover it is not forthcoming. This is where a leaflet given to the patient to take away at the time of the particular discussion is so useful. These leaflets fall into three categories:

1. Informative leaflets. These include information on fees, consumer's rights under the NHS and DHSS, vitreous floaters, accommodative squint, glaucoma, cataracts, driver's vision, industrial eye protection, etc.
2. Instructive leaflets. These may give guidance on orthoptic exercises, the use of low vision aids, how to care for new spectacles, etc.
3. Contact lens leaflets. These reinforce the advice on wearing and caring for the various types of contact lens materials, contact lens solutions, enzyme cleaning, the importance of regular aftercare visits, etc.

Mention must also be made here of the use of audiovisual presentations or 'videos'. These may be obtained through distributors such as Greames Optical Services Ltd, Halesowen, West Midlands, and cover such subjects as the routine eye examination and contact lens handling and care. The latter video could find a useful place in a busy contact lens practice as an introduction before the practical teaching begins. The new patient can sit back and watch the film (with his spectacles on!) to see well-performed insertion and removal before attempting it himself. A video on the eye examination could perhaps be most profitably shown to people who have never had their eyes examined at your practice before. Ideally, a room apart from reception is required and all new patients should be booked in five minutes earlier than usual for the presentation.

## Patients' complaints

As a general rule, all complaints should be taken very seriously. Of course, there are some people who make a habit of not being satisfied whatever you do, and you may well be better off if they drove another optometrist to distraction elsewhere. However, the majority of the public are reasonable people whose complaints change to misunderstandings when supplied with logical, straightforward explanations. Never forget that one unhappy patient is worth 50 satisfied ones. Most people expect good service and to be able to see comfortably and well with their new spectacles. They do not go around saying, 'Look at my new spectacles, and do you know what – I can see with them too!' *But*, if they do have any difficulty, it is likely to become their main topic of conversation until their problems are resolved. All the regulars in the local pub will be discussing your fitness to practise as an optometrist as long as you allow that patient to question your ability. Obviously this will not enhance your reputation.

Make sure you take the time to find out about individual complaints, or you will probably never hear about the majority of them if you have well-trained ancillary staff. This is for two reasons: either they will sort the problem out without reference to you or, by the time the patient sees you, he will have vented his anger on your assistants and will not even mention it to you. Yet the way your firm deals with complaints is one of the most important aspects of practice management. You must be seen not only to be fair and understanding, but also to 'go beyond the call of duty' to resolve the reason for the patient's dissatisfaction if you are to retain his patronage, and perhaps that of his family and friends. For this reason you must foster the best possible relationship between you and your assistants so that they know you will back them up at all times; then they will not be afraid to refer a complaint to you when either they find they cannot resolve it themselves or it is not a problem with which they should deal.

In a perfectly managed optometric practice grievances would never arise. The best way to work towards this ideal is to anticipate potential problems before they occur. Careful consideration of the following classification of complaints should help towards this end.

### *Appliances*

A patient should never have to return because a screw has fallen out of his frame. All screws should have a special adhesive such as Loctite on them before the spectacles are fitted. Particularly troublesome ones should be replaced with longer screws and 'burred over'.

Frames which acquire a poor reputation in your practice for durability, because they break easily or the gold plating is of poor quality, should cease to be stocked as soon as this becomes apparent. Any patients who complain that their frames have broken in an unreasonably short time (say, one year) should have them repaired or replaced at no charge, if it is plain that they have not been treated unreasonably. Since spectacles come under the terms of the Sale of Goods Act, patients are entitled to spectacles of 'merchantable quality', which means that they must be fit for the purpose for which they are prescribed. Let us assume you have dispensed a delicate rimless frame, with ordinary glass lenses for close work, to a man who works a drilling machine in a machine shop, without taking the trouble to determine his occupation or that he would be using the new spectacles at work. If the frames break, he may well have a case that the frames were not suitable for the purpose. He may even have a case under the Health and Safety at Work etc. Act in that they are not suitable eye protection. The frames are too weak and have no side shields, the lenses are not safety lenses, and you did not supply bifocals in order that he could walk about with them on instead of taking them off and losing their protection. Moral: determine exactly what the patient intends to use the appliance for during the consultation, and guide his choice of frames and lenses accordingly.

Keep your frame book up to date. It is frustrating for all concerned if a patient chooses a frame which is found to be discontinued only after you have ordered it. Sadly, with the introduction of high fashion frames and their short production runs, it could be argued that you should fit them only from stock. Nevertheless, this does not solve the problem of repairing them when the patient returns after only a few months, having broken a side, and spare parts are no longer available. Reputable frame manufacturers should not allow this to happen, but in any case let the spectacle shops, with their 'end-of-line' ranges and cheap imported frames, cope with the problem, not you.

### Delivery

Quote realistic delivery times. It is better to be resigned to a long wait from the outset than to be frustrated when the spectacles are long overdue. Naturally, perfectly justifiable reasons for delay do occur, such as lens breakages of complicated prescriptions. The golden rule is to contact the patient about the delay before he contacts you. Ask your assistants to keep you informed about all jobs outstanding by more than two days on any given day. Ensure that preferably the optometrist who examined the particular patient telephones him at the end of the day, apologises, gives the true reason for the delay and a revised delivery date. Then keep a special watch on that job. This all helps foster the impression that you care about the individual patient for his own sake rather than just as a means of making a living.

As regards the notification of patients that their spectacles are ready, it is tempting to assume that they are being awkward if they do not immediately come and have them fitted after you send the card. But cards get lost in the post. You may have an old address on the record, especially if the job is a repair and the patient has not had his eyes examined for several years. It is always best to notify by telephone and speak to the patient himself so that an approximate time for fitting can also be arranged if required. It is quicker if all notifications are left until the end of the day; also the telephone charges are less.

## Repairs

Patients often complain that they cannot manage without their spectacles while you send them away for repair. This would not be a problem if all patients had spare spectacles, and perhaps this should be mentioned during the eye examination. However, given that the patient has no spare spectacles, everything should be done to 'keep him going' while a permanent solution is sought. The lenses can be transferred into another frame, or bridges can be sewn and odd sides can be put on whilst a new frame is ordered. Whatever happens, do everything in your power to keep the patient seeing, even if it means sending an assistant to the local prescription house with the job for repair while she waits. Of course, if you have facilities for in-house glazing and repairs, this problem is easily resolved.

## Fitting of spectacles and adapting to new prescriptions

Complaints under this heading can usually be handled by your assistant in the first instance. If the spectacles hurt or slip, then a minor adjustment is probably all that is required. Queries about distorted vision, adapting to bifocals, sloping floors, etc. are usually resolved by a little encouragement and reassurance that it often takes a few days to adapt to the new 'visual environment' created by a change in prescription. If this is a fairly frequent complaint, it indicates that you are not explaining clearly enough the full consequences of a new prescription to the patient before he leaves the consulting room.

Should the patient return a second time with the same difficulties, the assistant must refer him back to the prescribing practitioner. The wide variation amongst individuals in their ability to adapt to new prescriptions must alway be borne in mind. It is one thing to determine the lenses which give a person the best acuity, but quite another to decide the best prescription to actually give the patient. The only real way is the hard way: by experience and learning by your mistakes. But there are some guidelines:

1. The older a person is, the more resistant to change he is likely to be, so think twice about prescribing bifocals to a 65-year-old for the first time, or changing a 3 dioptre cylinder through 30 degrees, even it is does improve the acuity to 6/6. Give a compromise, perhaps 20 degrees, and get the patient to return in six months to complete the change.
2. Do not, as a rule, change the spectacles of a diabetic if he is not stabilised or has found sugar in his urine that day – the prescription is bound to change.
3. Make certain that a wearer of hard contact lenses appreciates that, whatever spectacle prescription you make up, he is unlikely to be entirely happy with the acuity they provide, due to the corneal distortion produced by the contact lenses.
4. If a patient has had natural 'monovision' for years (i.e. he has been using one eye for distance and the other for reading), do not force spectacles on him in the hope that he will use his eyes together. Almost certainly he will prefer to carry on without any correction rather than have to cope with the disadvantages of either two pairs of spectacles or bifocals (or, possibly, double vision).

5. Do not, as a matter of principle, force all presbyopes to have reading spectacles. Perhaps the only demands they make on their vision are for shopping, playing cards, using a VDU, playing a musical instrument, do-it-yourself or cutting their toenails, in which case an intermediate prescription would be more appropriate.

6. If it is obvious that a pre-presbyopic hyperope does not, or will not, wear his correction all the time, reduce it by about 10–25 per cent to allow a little active accommodation; otherwise, he will have difficulty seeing clearly either when he first puts his spectacles on or when he takes them off.

7. Consider very carefully increasing the reading add by more than +0.50 D, even if the patient has not had his eyes examined for years and it really takes another +1.00 D for him to read N5. He will appreciate the improvement in reading that +0.50 brings, without the dramatic reduction in depth of field of his optimum near correction. Again, bring him back in six months to complete the transition.

8. Do not put a prism in a lens with a fixed tint – the wearer will experience multiple images.

9. Always check the base curves, as well as the centration distance of the lenses, if a patient complains he cannot see as clearly with a duplicate prescription. If the problem is traced to the base curves, make a note on the record that the original curves should be duplicated in future. For this reason, be particularly wary of changing to a lens of different refractive index in future with such patients.

10. If the patient still complains of bowed straight lines and edges with a duplicate pair of lenses and you have checked the powers, the centration distances and the base curves and considered the refractive index of the material, the trouble must lie in the frontal angle of the frame. Match this to the old spectacles and the difficulty should finally disappear.

Above all, as has been said before, try to prevent any complaints about non-tolerance by always discussing and demonstrating the prescription you propose to dispense to a patient, and do not go ahead unless he feels the improvement is worthwhile after considering the cost and any drawbacks the prescription may have.

### Miscellaneous complaints

Some people expect to be seen either immediately or at least the same day as they make the appointment. Of course, this may be possible if the practice is new, or there is a cancellation, or the assistant feels that it is an emergency because the patient may be suffering from an eye disease or he has completely broken or lost his only pair of spectacles. On the other hand, if it is just a routine appointment and the person still refuses to comprehend why he cannot be seen immediately, even after the reasons have been carefully explained to him, do not be tempted to see him in case he goes elsewhere. Let him go anyway. Apart from the insult to the following patients by delaying them – even though they may have had to wait weeks to consult you – the 'gatecrasher' will always expect the same treatment in future, and will be a constant irritation.

Optometrists are increasingly being blamed for profiteering on contact lens solutions. This view is as potentially dangerous as it is untrue. The danger comes from patients deciding that the solutions have become too expensive and either not changing them often enough or not using them at all. Once again, honesty is the best policy, and the running costs of contact lens wear should be realistically discussed at the initial fitting appointment. Patients must be made to understand that they are paying the price of safety. Now that contact lens solutions have come under the control of the Medicines Act with its strict rules on their preparation and bottling, the cost of the production of contact lens solutions has increased sharply – but all in the interests of safety to the wearer.

## Unreasonable complaints

There are some complaints where it is dangerous to apply the old adage 'the customer is always correct'. They invariably concern the breakage of spectacles or contact lenses. Occasionally a patient appears at reception with spectacles that have obviously been sat on, if not jumped on. Probably one side is broken off and a lens is cracked. You are told that they were perfectly all right when the patient put them on the bedside table the night before, but, on waking, they were in their present state. Obviously, there was a fault in their manufacture, and you are told to provide a replacement pair, at no charge, within 24 hours. It is also becoming increasingly common with the newer, more fragile, contact lens materials for patients to find their lenses mysteriously broken when they open the case in the morning. Again, faulty manufacture is blamed, and a replacement lens, at no charge, is demanded. If you try to explain that, although the material is easily broken, it cannot self-destruct, you risk being asked if you are calling the patient a liar and, anyway, even if the patient did break it accidentally, it 'obviously is not suitable for the purpose for which it is designed – Sale of Goods Act' and a fresh demand is made for 'another lens or my money back'. All of which is upsetting for you and your assistants, not to mention embarrassing if there are patients within earshot, which there invariably are on such occasions.

Stay calm. Say you are perfectly willing to send the broken spectacles or contact lenses back to the manufacturers, although you feel that the chances of their admitting responsibility are not high. However, tell him that when you receive a reply, you will contact him or send him a copy. Meanwhile, ask him if he would like to pay for the repair or replacement, on the basis that you will refund the money if the manufacturers do admit liability.

In other words, think very carefully before you give things away. Take each case on its merits. If a patient has always been reasonable in the past, paid his account promptly and has a complaint with which you have some sympathy, you will probably want to replace the appliance at little or no charge because you feel sorry for him. This is fine and demonstrates your concern for the individual patient. Make sure, however, that he understands what you are doing, and that obviously your generosity cannot be repeated or you would go bankrupt if you gave everything away. The unreasonable, bombastic complainant is a different kettle of fish. If you surrender just once to his demands, you will be creating a precedent he will never forget, and he will expect something for nothing for ever.

## Infamous conduct

The question of protection from a patient's charge of infamous conduct should be borne in mind. Most of the work of an optometrist is done in a room alone with the patient. It is carried out behind closed doors and often with the light out. These conditions are ideal for malicious or imagined claims of misconduct. Although the risk cannot be entirely eliminated, it can be reduced. An optometric assistant could be asked to stay in the consulting room throughout the examination or during part of it. Certainly all members of staff, professional or not, should be instructed to knock and enter consulting rooms without waiting for a reply. A 'panic button' could be installed within easy reach of the practitioner and instructions given that, if used, other staff must immediately go to the consulting room and enter without knocking.

One last point. There is a story about an optometrist who had his ophthalmoscope powered by a transformer and hence had a trailing cable. One day, an imaginative young lady felt the cable trailing across her legs in the dark as the optometrist moved around her. She jumped to completely the wrong conclusion. Moral: use only rechargeable or battery handles on retinoscopes and ophthalmoscopes or find a good solicitor!

# References and further reading

**Statutes**

Partnership Act 1890
Sale of Goods Act 1893
Limited Partnerships Act 1907
Registration of Business Names Act 1916
Factories Act 1937
National Health Service Act 1946
National Health Service (Scotland) Act 1947
Health Services (Northern Ireland) Act 1947
Nurseries and Child-Minders Regulation Act 1948
National Assistance Act 1948
Companies Act 1948
National Health Service (Amendment) Act 1949
Shops Act 1950
National Health Service Act 1951
National Health Service Act 1952
Opticians Act 1958
Factories Act 1961
National Health Service Act 1961
Offices, Shops and Railway Premises Act 1963
Shops (Early Closing Days) Act 1965
Companies Act 1967
Misrepresentation Act 1967
Trade Descriptions Act 1968
Health Services and Public Health Act 1968
Medicines Act 1968
Employers Liability (Compulsory Insurance) Act 1969
Equal Pay Act 1970
Misuse of Drugs Act 1971
Fire Precautions Act 1971
Road Traffic Act 1972
National Health Service Reorganisation Act 1973
Health and Safety at Work etc. Act 1974

Sex Discrimination Act 1975
National Health Service Act 1977
Employment Protection (Consolidation) Act 1978
Health Services Act 1980
Health and Social Security Act 1984

## Statutory instruments

| | |
|---|---|
| 1922/731 | Chemical Works Regulations |
| 1953/1464 | Iron and Steel Foundries Regulations |
| 1956/1077 | National Health Service (Service Committees and Tribunal) Regulations |
| 1956/1078 | National Health Service (Supplementary Ophthalmic Services) Regulations |
| 1960/1932 | Shipbuilding and Ship-Repairing Regulations |
| 1960/1934 | General Optical Council (Disciplinary Committee Rules) Order of Council |
| 1960/1935 | General Optical Council (Investigating Committee Rules) Order of Council |
| 1960/1936 | General Optical Council (Rules Relating to Injury or Disease of the Eye) Order of Council |
| 1961/1239 | General Optical Council Disciplinary Committee (Legal Assessor) Rules |
| 1961/1580 | Construction (General Provisions) Regulations |
| 1961/1933 | General Optical Council (Disciplinary Committee) Procedure Order of Council |
| 1962/1667 | Non-ferrous metals (Melting and Founding) Regulations |
| 1964/167 | General Optical Council (Rules on Publicity) Order of Council |
| 1965/1366 | National Health Service (Service Committees and Tribunal) Amendment Regulations |
| 1969/354 | National Health Service (Service Committees and Tribunal) (Amendment) Regulations |
| 1969/1826 | General Optical Council (Disciplinary Committee) (Procedure) Order of Council |
| 1974/287 | National Health Service (General Ophthalmic Services) Regulations |
| 1974/455 | National Health Service (Service Committees and Tribunal) Regulations |
| 1974/527 | National Health Service (General Ophthalmic Services) (Amendment) Regulations |
| 1974/907 | National Health Service (Service Committees and Tribunal) Amendment Regulations |
| 1974/1681 | Protection of Eyes Regulations |
| 1975/789 | (s. 129) National Health Service (General Ophthalmic Services) (S.) (Amendment) Regulations |
| 1976/303 | Protection of Eyes (Amendment) Regulations |
| 1976/2010 | Fire Precautions (Non-Certificated Factory, Office, Shop and Railway Premises) Regulations |
| 1977/434 | National Health Service (Charges and Remission) Amendment Regulations |

1977/1999   National Health Service (General Ophthalmic Services) Amendment Regulations
1977/2127   Medicines (Prescription Only) Order
1977/2129   Medicines (General Sale List) Order
1977/2132   Medicines (Sale or Supply) (Miscellaneous Provisions) Regulations
1977/2133   Medicines (Pharmacy and General Sale – Exemption) Order
1978/950    National Health Service (Dental and Optical Charges) Regulations
1978/987    Medicines (Prescription Only) Amendment (No. 2) Order
1978/988    Medicines (Pharmacy and General Sale – Exemption) Amendment Order
1978/989    Medicines (Sale or Supply) (Miscellaneous Provisions) Amendment Regulations
1980/1921   Medicines (Prescription Only) Order
1980/1922   Medicines (General Sale List) Order
1980/1923   Medicines (Sale or Supply) Miscellaneous Provisions Regulations
1980/1924   Medicines (Pharmacy and General Sale – Exemption) Order
1981/552    General Optical Council (Rules of Publicity) Order of Council
1981/952    Motor Vehicles (Driving Licences) Regulations
1983/1212   Medicines (Products Other Than Veterinary Drugs) (Prescription Only) Order
1984/1778   Sale of Optical Appliances Order of Council
1985/203    General Optical Council (Rules on Publicity) Order of Council
1985/298    National Health Service (General Ophthalmic Services) Amendment Regulations
1985/856    General Optical Council (Rules on Fitting Contact Lenses) Order of Council

## Books and journals

COLE, J. (1979) The Thiriart Report – an assessment of optometry in Europe. *Optician,* **17**, May 11, 13–17

DRASDO, N. and HAGGERTY, C. M. (1981) A comparison of the British number-plate and Snellen vision test for car drivers. *Ophthalmic and Physiological Optics,* **1**, 39–54

HOFSTETTER, H. W. (1976) Optometry on the Continent. 2. Belgium. *Optician,* **172**, Oct 8, 8–9

HOFSTETTER, H. W. (1976) Optometry on the Continent. 3. Denmark. *Optician,* **172**, Oct 22, 25–27

HOFSTETTER, H. W. (1976) Optometry on the Continent. 6. France. *Optician,* **172**, Dec 10, 13–15

HOFSTETTER, H. W. (1976) Optometry on the Continent. 7. Italy. *Optician,* **172**, Dec 24/31, 16–25

HOFSTETTER, H. W. (1977) Optometry on the Continent. 8. Netherlands. *Optician,* **173**, Jan 28, 11–15

HOFSTETTER, H. W. (1977) Optometry on the Continent. 11. West Germany. *Optician,* **173**, Mar 25, 18–35

KLEIN, P. (1983) Why I have a finishing lab. *Review of Optometry,* November, 37–43

KOCH, C. C. (1947) British reaction to the National Health Insurance scheme. *American Journal of Optometrists and Archives of the Academy of Optometrists,* **24**, 151–169

NEW ZEALAND OPTOMETRICAL ASSOCIATION (1969) *Design for Optometric Premises.* Wellington: NZOA

NOIR, C. (1984) Security and the practice. *Optician,* **188**, Jul 27, 10–13

O'CONNOR DAVIES, P. H. (1978) Medicines legislation and the ophthalmic optician. *Ophthalmic Optician,* **18**, 688–694

O'CONNOR DAVIES, P. H. (1980) The use of ophthalmic drugs in the United Kingdom. *American Journal of Optometry and Physiological Optics,* **57**, 925–926

OFFICE OF FAIR TRADING (1982) *Opticians and Competition.* London: HMSO

PA MANAGEMENT CONSULTANTS (1982) *The Kelvin Handbook of Optical Practice Management*. Manchester: PA Management Consultants Ltd

REDMOND, P. W. D. (1970) *General Principles of English Law*. London: Macdonald & Evans

ROUSSELL, D. F. (1979) *Eye Protection*. Birmingham: Royal Society for the Prevention of Accidents

SASIENI, L. S. (1981a) A guide to the practitioner's glazing workshop. *Optician*, **181**, Jun 19, 14–16

SASIENI, L. S. (1981b) A guide to the well equipped practice. *Optician*, **181**, Jan 9, 11–20

SEATON, C. R. (1966) *Aspects of the National Health Service Acts*. London: Pergamon Press

SIMMONDS, A. B. (1981) The attitude of the public towards the optometric profession. *Optician*, **181**, Jun 26, 22–28

STEIN, H. A. and SLATT, B. J. (1983) *The Ophthalmic Assistant: fundamentals and clinical practice*, 4th edn. St Louis, Missouri: C. V. Mosby

TAYLOR, S. P. (1982) Ophthalmic law. *Optician*, **188**, no. 4757, 10

TAYLOR, S. P. (1983) New York State optometry: its legislation and practice. *Optician*, **186**, no. 4820, 11–12

TAYLOR, S. P. (1984) Advertising – a professional spectacle. *Optician*, **187**, no. 4930, 10–13

WAUD, C. (1982) *Redundancy and Unfair Dismissal*. London: Harmsworth

WILDING, N. and LAUNDY, P. (1961) *An Encyclopaedia of Parliament*. London: Cassell

YARMOVSKY, R. (1984) The legal diversification of optometry. *Journal of the American Optometric Association*, **55**, 665–669

YEOMANS, F. (1984) Optometry in West Germany. *Optician*, **188**, no. 4966, 31–35

# Case records

One area of practice which receives far less attention than it deserves is case records. It is the case record which can make or break a case of negligence. A sad finding from visiting many different practices is the total inadequacy of many records. It is likely that most practitioners would not consider that they themselves are inadequate record keepers but this appendix, by outlining the bare minimum contents and demonstrating the essential elements of a record, may make them think again.

Record cards are intended to carry information pertinent to the patient's problems. They also act as a reminder to the practitioner of findings of an earlier examination and provide a means of evaluating change in basic measurements. The exact style of the record card is left to the practitioner – some consisting simply of blank areas, others listing some of the more useful and usual measurements and some providing enough space to include more detailed but less important information such as the number of children the patient has, whether any children are going to university or taking up new jobs, if the patient has a particular hobby and what the patient is hoping to do for a holiday.

Whatever the style of the record to be used, there are some basic points which should always be included.

### Personal details

*Name* There are few records which do not carry the patient's name. It is important, however, that the full name is recorded and not just initials. From a filing point of view it can be an absolute nightmare trying to locate a Mr Jones in South Wales without the full name.

*Address* This also is absolutely essential and should be updated whenever the patient points out a change.

*Telephone number* It helps immensely if a patient can be reached by telephone during the day. For example, if something goes wrong with the promised job, you can advise the patient before he has to chase you.

*Date of birth*   The full date of birth is particularly necessary where, for example, father and son have the same names and live at the same address.

*Date of examination*   There is nothing more irritating for a patient who asks for the date of the last examination than to be told 'Oh, it was about 1983'. From a legal standpoint, the date of examination could be an important factor in deciding whether or not a condition should have been noted at that time.

*Occupation*   It is usually necessary to know the patient's occupation. If glasses are prescribed for a specific occupation, they may prove totally unsuitable if the patient decides to change jobs.

*General practitioner's name and address*   This information should be recorded for two reasons. First, it is needed for referral letters; secondly, if, as sometimes happens, a health clinic contacts the practice to ask for information about a particular patient, you can find out with whom you are dealing.

*Hobbies*   This information is necessary to help with the best choice of correction.

## Clinical details from patient

*Case history*   Has the patient had an eye examination previously? If so, were spectacles prescribed and, if so, for what were they to be used? Has the patient ever had any eye injury or operation and, if so, what was its nature?

*Symptoms*   Why has the patient decided to visit an ophthalmic optician/optometrist? Does he suffer from eye ache or headaches? When do the symptoms occur?

*General health*   Is the patient suffering from any general disorder or taking any tablets, pills or other medication?

*Family history*   Is there any history of eye problems or of general health problems in the family?

## Examination details

*Unaided vision*

*Retinoscopy*

*Subjective*

*Best corrected distance acuity*

*Distance muscle balance, etc.*

*Amplitude of accommodation*

*Near acuity*

*Near reading correction*, if necessary

*Near muscle balance*

*External examination of the eyes*

*Ophthalmoscopy*  It is important that the case record shows that a full examination has been carried out. It may be adequate to write 'NAD' in this section but this does not show that you actually examined any particular structure. A complete record should carry information such as: 'media clear, discs flat, cup/disc 0.2, fundus clear'; this at least shows that structures were examined.

*Supplementary tests* carried out

*Decision on patient disposal*  This should include a copy of the referral note if the patient is advised to visit his general practitioner, or the patient's signature if such advice is rejected.

*Examiner's name*

**Dispensing details**

*Distance*  Frame details, facial measurements and centration distance

*Near*  Frame details and centration distance

**Costing**

This comprises the charges and fees, and details of any deposit.

The above outline simply presents the basic type of information required; it does not offer a layout and it does not offer any advice on the relative importance of each category. Many ophthalmic opticians/optometrists will already use a case record which carries more information. In the present circumstances where the professional activity of ophthalmic opticians/optometrists is under scrutiny it is essential that every effort be made to protect one's clinical reputation. Complete and accurate case records are a simple and effective way of achieving this. An example of a case record which incorporates most of the above is given in *Figure A1.1*.

Name                                    Address

| Date : | | N.H.S. No. | | Tele. No. | |
|---|---|---|---|---|---|
| Age : | | D.O.B. : | | | ↓  Lenses |
| Refractionist : | V      R | | | V.A. | |
| | V      L | | | V.A. | |
| Retinoscopy : | | R.E. | | L.E. | |
| | | Rdg./Work | | | |
| N.P.C. | | Amp : Of Accommodation · | | | |
| Frames : Dist. : | | | | | |
| | | | | | Fees & Charges |
| Rdg. : | | | | | |
| | | | | Total | |
| | | | | Deposit | |
| Job Nos. | | | | Balance | |

Doctor's Name & Address :

Symptoms, Case History,

& Health

Fundus : & External

| Muscle Balance : | | Dist. : | | Near : | |
|---|---|---|---|---|---|
| Amplitude/Ductions/Vergences/Orthoptics | | | T/ | | |
| Occupation   & Hobbies | | | | | |

Repairs :

| Request for | 1st Reminder | 2nd Reminder |
|---|---|---|
| | | |

*Figure A1.1* An example of a case record card

## Appendix 2

# Commonly used ophthalmic drugs and their legal classification

| Drug | Legal class. | | Optometrist: | |
|---|---|---|---|---|
| | *POM* | *P* | *Uses* | *Supplies* |
| Adrenaline | | + | + | |
| Adrenaline acid tartrate | | + | + | |
| Adrenaline hydrochloride | | + | + | |
| Amethocaine | + | | + | |
| Amethocaine hydrochloride | + | | + | |
| Antazoline (to 1%) | | + | + | |
| Artificial tears | | + | + | + |
| Atropine | + | | + | + |
| Atropine methobromide | + | | + | + |
| Atropine methonitrate | + | | + | + |
| Atropine sulphate | + | | + | + |
| Bethanecol chloride | + | | + | + |
| Butacaine sulphate | + | | + | |
| Carbachol | + | | + | + |
| Cyclopentolate hydrochloride | + | | + | + |
| Dibromopropamidine isethionate (Brolene Ointment) | | + | + | + |
| Ecothiopate iodide | + | | + | + |
| Ephedrine | + | | + | |
| Ephedrine hydrochloride | + | | + | |
| Ephedrine sulphate | + | | + | |
| Fluorescein sodium | | + | + | + |
| Framycetin sulphate | + | | + | |
| Golden eye ointment | | + | + | |
| Homatropine hydrobromide | + | | + | + |
| Hyoscine hydrobromide | + | | + | + |
| Lignocaine hydrochloride | + | | + | |
| Mafenide propionate (less than 5%) | | + | + | + |
| Mafenide propionate (more than 5%) | + | | + | + |
| Methacholine chloride (Amechol) | | + | + | + |
| Naphazoline hydrochloride (less than 0.015%) | | + | + | |
| Naphazoline nitrate | + | | + | + |
| Neostigmine methylsulphate | + | | + | + |
| Oxybuprocaine hydrochloride | + | | + | |
| Oxyphenbutazone ointment | + | | + | |
| Phenacaine | + | | + | |
| Phenylephrine hydrochloride | | + | + | |
| Physostigmine | + | | + | + |
| Physostigmine salicylate | + | | + | + |
| Physostigmine sulphate | + | | + | + |
| Pilocarpine nitrate | + | | + | + |
| Propamidine isethionate (Brolene Eye Drops) | | + | + | + |
| Proxymetacaine hydrochloride | + | | + | |
| Sulphacetamide sodium (up to 30%) | + | | + | + |
| Sulphafurazole diethanolamine (up to 40%) | + | | + | + |
| Thymoxamine hydrochloride | + | | + | |
| Tropicamide | + | | + | |
| Zinc sulphate | | + | + | |

P, pharmacy medicines; POM, prescription only medicines

# Appendix 3
# National Health Service forms

NHS GENERAL OPHTHALMIC SERVICES        SIGHT TESTING        GOS2A(1)
PLEASE USE BLOCK LETTERS EXCEPT FOR SIGNATURES

SURNAME (MR/MRS/MISS/MS)        DATE OF BIRTH (IF UNDER 19)    /    /

OTHER NAME(S)        DATE OF LAST SIGHT TEST    /    /

ADDRESS

As far as I know, the information I have given on this form is true and complete. I apply for a NHS sight test.

PATIENT'S SIGNATURE ........................................................................ Date ............ / ...... / ............

(or, in the case of a child under 16 or an invalid, the signature of parent/guardian/other person in charge.)

Name of Ophthalmic Medical Practitioner, Ophthalmic Optician who tested the patient's sight, and address at which it was done (block letters or stamp)

This patient's sight was tested on ................................................(date) with the following outcome (tick as appropriate)

☐ No prescription required

☐ GOS2A(2) handed to patient with new prescription

☐ GOS2A(2) handed to patient with unchanged prescription

Additional remarks (non-tolerance claimed, early retest advised, patient referred to general practitioner etc):–

Name and address of contractor to whom payment should be made (block letters or stamp)

...of the appropriate fee

...IC LIS...

Printed in the U.K. for H.M.S.O. Dd. 8884903 50m pads 3/85

NHS GENERAL OPHTHALMIC ...        ...RIPTION        GOS2A(2)
PLEASE USE BLOCK LETTERS ...FOR S...

SURNAME (MR/MRS/MISS/MS)        DATE OF BIRTH (IF UNDER 19)    /    /

OTHER NAME(S)

ADDRESS

| RIGHT | Sph | Cyl | Axis | Prism | Base | | Sph | Cyl | Axis | Prism | Base | LEFT |
|---|---|---|---|---|---|---|---|---|---|---|---|---|
| | | | | | | Distance | | | | | | |
| | | | | | | Near | | | | | | |

Any other relevant details

FOR USE OF DISPENSER
Date of any NHS dispensing
to this prescription

I have today [Date      ] conducted a sight test
with the result shown above which represents
(tick as appropriate)

☐ a new prescription

☐ an unchanged prescription

☐ complex prescription for NHS purposes

NAME AND PRACTICE ADDRESS (BLOCK LETTERS OR STAMP)

Signature ....................................................................

Ophthalmic List No. ....................................................................

**KEEP THIS PRESCRIPTION IN A SAFE PLACE FOR USE TO OBTAIN GLASSES
OR IN CASE OF ANY DIFFICULTIES**

— Most people now need to obtain their glasses privately.

— If you are aged 16 or over, you may take this prescription to any registered optician or other supplier of glasses for dispensing. Only registered opticians may dispense glasses for people aged under 16.

— Children under 16, full-time students under 19, people on certain benefits and others on low incomes may, however, still obtain glasses under the NHS.

— People with complex prescriptions for NHS purposes (see overleaf) can also obtain their glasses under the NHS.

— For full details of eligibility for NHS glasses, see leaflet G11.

**GENERAL OPHTHALMIC SERVICES**                    **GOS2B(1)**

## Entitlement to the supply of glasses under the National Health Service

SURNAME (MR/MRS/MISS/MS) _____   DATE OF BIRTH (If under 19)   /   /

OTHER NAME(S) _____

ADDRESS _____

The list below shows the description of people who are entitled to glasses under the National Health Service. If any descriptions apply to you or to the person who supports you, please tick the appropriate boxes:–

|  |  | This applies to the patient | This applies to the person who supports the patient |
|---|---|---|---|
| 1 | getting a regular supplementary pension or allowance or housing benefit *supplement* | ☐ | ☐ |
| 2 | getting Family Income Supplement (FIS) | | ☐ |
| 3 | has a valid certificate of exemption from prescription ch~~___~~ income | | ☐ |
| 4 | is a member of a family of which the sa~~___~~ or a~~___~~ free milk and vitamins on *income gro___* | | |
| 5 | under 16 | ☐ | |
| 6 | over 16 and under 19 and still in full ti~~___~~ .................................... ..........................................(enter~~___~~ of school/college/university) | ☐ | |
| 7 | has Form F3 (0) which confirms that the conditions for receiving NHS glasses on low income grounds are satisfied | ☐ | |
| 8 | satisfies the special arrangements for the supply of complex lenses. Check with your optician (full charges are payable unless any of the other circumstances above also apply) | ☐ | |

If you have ticked any of the boxes for the person who supports you, please give his/her name below:-

NAME ..................................................................................................

Remember – if you deliberately give false information or withhold information, you may be prosecuted.

DECLARATION –  As far as I know, the information I have given on this form is true and complete. I apply for supply of glasses under the NHS and will pay any charge which is necessary in my circumstances.

Signature ............................................................... Date ...................................

(or, in the case of a child under 16 or an invalid, signature of parent/guardian/other person in charge)

PRINTED IN THE UK FOR HMSO. Dd. 8884904. 22,500 Pads. 3 85. 49261

 **SUPPLY OF GLASSES**                    GOS2B(2)

DETAILS OF PRESCRIPTION

| | Sph | Cyl | Axis | Prism | Base | | Sph | Cyl | Axis | Prism | Base | |
|---|---|---|---|---|---|---|---|---|---|---|---|---|
| **RIGHT** | | | | | | Distance | | | | | | **LEFT** |
| | | | | | | Near | | | | | | |

ANY OTHER RELEVANT DETAILS FROM THE PRESCRIPTION

DETAILS OF PRESCRIBER IN CASES WHERE NOT DISPENSER

Name                                                                Ophthalmic List No.

Address

DESCRIPTION OF GLASSES SUPPLIED

| FIRST PAIR | DESCRIPTION | Price £ | p |
|---|---|---|---|
| Lens(es) | RIGHT | | |
| | LEFT | | |
| Extras | RIGHT | | |
| | LEFT | | |
| FRAME | ☐ New NHS type . . . | | |
| | ☐ Reglazed NHS | | |
| | ☐ Reglazed Private | | |
| | ☐ New Private | | |

| SECOND PAIR | | | |
|---|---|---|---|
| Lens(es) | RIGHT | | |
| | LEFT | | |
| Extras | RIGHT | | |
| | LEFT | | |
| FRAME | ☐ New NHS type . . . | | |
| | ☐ Reglazed NHS | | |
| | ☐ Reglazed Private | | |
| | ☐ New Private | | |

| CASES | |
|---|---|
| SUB-TOTAL | |
| Dispensing fee(s) | |
| FIRST PAIR | |
| SECOND PAIR | |
| GROSS TOTAL A | |

PATIENT'S CHARGES
(INC. PAYABLE EXTRAS)                          £          p

| | £ | p |
|---|---|---|
| Lens(es) 1st pair | | |
| Lens(es) 2nd pair | | |
| Frame 1st pair | | |
| Frame 2nd pair | | |
| Total | | |
| Sub-total to pay F3(O) plus payable extras | | |

OPTICIAN'S CLAIM

Gross Total (A opposite)              £ . . . . . . . . . . . .

Less (x) or (y) above                  £ . . . . . . . . . . . .

NET CLAIM                              £

I have carried out the supply described above and claim payment of the net amount shown.

SIGNATURE . . . . . . . . . . . . . . . . . . . . . . . . . . . . . . . . . . .

OPHTHALMIC LIST NO. . . . . . . . . . . . . . . . . . . . . . . . .

DATE . . . . . . . . . . . . . . . . . . . . . . . .

NAME AND ADDRESS OF CONTRACTOR TO WHOM PAYMENT SHOULD BE MADE

I confirm that the glasses as described above have been supplied, that any charges payable have been explained to me, and that I have been offered a receipt for any charges I have paid.

Signature of patient . . . . . . . . . . . . . . . . . . . . . . . . . . . . . . . . . . . . . . . . . . . . . . . . . . .   Date . . . . . . . . . . . . . . . . . .
(or, in the case of a child under 16 or an invalid, signature of parent/guardian/other person in charge)

**GENERAL OPHTHALMIC SERVICES**                    **GOS2R(1)**

## Entitlement to the repair or replacement of glasses under the National Health Service

| SURNAME (MR/MRS/MISS/MS) | DATE OF BIRTH (If under 19)    /    / |
|---|---|

OTHER NAME(S)

ADDRESS

The list below shows the descriptions of people who are entitled to the repair or replacement of glasses supplied under the National Health Service. If any descriptions apply to you or to the person who supports you, please tick the appropriate boxes:—

|  | | This applies to the patient | This applies to the person who supports the patient |
|---|---|---|---|
| **1** | getting a regular supplementary pension or allowance or housing benefit *supplement* | ☐ | ☐ |
| **2** | getting Family Income Supplement (FIS) | | ☐ |
| **3** | has a valid certificate of exemption from prescription charges because of low income | | ☐ |
| **4** | is a member of a family of which the same or another ... free milk and vitamins on *income grounds* | ☐ | |
| **5** | under 16 | | |
| **6** | over 16 and under 19 and st... ...e an... ...sc... ...university) | ☐ | |
| **7** | has Form F3 (0) which confirm... ...nd... ...g NHS glasses on low income grounds are satis... | ☐ | |
| **8** | satisfies the special arrangements ...ly ... complex lenses. Check with your optician (full charges are p... ...less any of the other circumstances above also apply) | ☐ | |
| **9** | believes that he/she will be eligible for NHS provision on low income grounds but has either not yet been notified of the outcome of a claim or has not yet had the opportunity to apply *and needs his/her glasses repaired or replaced as an emergency* | ☐ | |

If you have ticked any of the boxes for the person who supports you, please give his/her name below:-

NAME .................................................................................................

This applies only to applicants who have ticked items 7 and 9 above – if you claim that the loss or damage to your glasses was not caused through your fault, please describe the circumstances.

Remember – if you deliberately give false information or withhold information, you may be prosecuted.

**DECLARATION –** As far as I know, the information I have given on this form is true and complete. I apply for repair or replacement of glasses which were supplied under the NHS and have been lost, destroyed or damaged and will pay any charge which is necessary in my circumstances.

Signature ...................................................................................... Date ....................................
(or, in the case of a child under 16 or an invalid, signature of parent/guardian/other person in charge)

**REPAIR OR REPLACEMENT OF GLASSES**    **GOS2R(2)**

DETAILS OF PRESCRIPTION

| | Sph | Cyl | Axis | Prism | Base | | | Sph | Cyl | Axis | Prism | Base | |
|---|---|---|---|---|---|---|---|---|---|---|---|---|---|
| **RIGHT** | | | | | | ⊠ | Distance | | | | | | **LEFT** |
| | | | | | | | Near | | | | | | |

ANY OTHER RELEVANT DETAILS FROM THE PRESCRIPTION

DESCRIPTION OF GLASSES SUPPLIED

| DESCRIPTION | | Price £ | p |
|---|---|---|---|
| Lens(es) | RIGHT | | |
| | LEFT | | |
| Extras | RIGHT | | |
| | LEFT | | |

FRAME

- ☐ New NHS . . . . . . Frame/front/side
- ☐ Reglazed NHS
- ☐ Reglazed Private
- ☐ New Private

| | | |
|---|---|---|
| CASE | | |
| SUB-TOTAL | | |
| Dispensing or service fee | | |
| GROSS TOTAL A | | |

PATIENT'S CHARGES (INC. PAYABLE EXTRAS)

| | | £ | p |
|---|---|---|---|
| Lens(es) | | | |
| Frame | | | |
| Total | | | |
| to patient plus payable extras | | | |

OPTICIAN'S CLAIM

Gross Total (A opposite)    £ ..........................

Less (x) or (y) above    £ ..........................

NET CLAIM    £

I have carried out the replacement or repair described above and claim payment of the net amount shown.

SIGNATURE ................................................

OPHTHALMIC LIST NO. ................................

DATE ................................................

I confirm that the repair or replacement described above has been carried out, that any charges payable have been explained to me and that I have been offered a receipt for any charges paid.

Signature of patient ................................................

Date ................................................

(or, in the case of a child under 16 or an invalid, signature of parent/guardian/other person in charge)

NAME AND ADDRESS OF CONTRACTOR TO WHOM PAYMENT SHOULD BE MADE

Printed in the UK for HMSO Dd.8884905  3/85  (11037)

SAMPLE

FORM GOS 15    SERIAL No. **09745550**

**NATIONAL HEALTH SERVICE**
**GENERAL OPHTHALMIC SERVICES**
**SUPPLY, REPLACEMENT OR REPAIR OF GLASSES**

I have today received from

M ...........................................................................

of ...........................................................................

...........................................................................

...........................................................................

the sum of £......... in respect of NHS frame No............

the sum of £......... in respect of NHS standard lenses

the sum of £......... in respect of other items, viz;

    TOTAL £

Date................. Signature.....................................

| Name and address of optician |
| --- |
|  |

**NOTES FOR THE PATIENT**

1. If your income is low you may be entitled to repayment of any charges you have paid for NHS frames and NHS standard lenses (but not any other items). If you would like to claim, ask the local office of the Department of Health and Social Security for Form F6.

2. If you have any other query about the charges you have paid for the supply, replacement or repair of glasses under the National Health Service, ask your optician or the local Family Practitioner Committee: their address and telephone number may be obtained from the telephone directory or any main Post Office.

Dd086244 6602079 10m 9/76 J.I.H. Ltd., 27081            G.O.S. 18

## N.H.S. GENERAL OPHTHALMIC SERVICES

Reference of patient back to General Medical Practitioner

**SECTION 1.** To be completed by Ophthalmic Medical Practitioner/Ophthalmic Optician

Patient: Mr./Mrs./Miss....................................................    O.M.P.'s/O.O.'s Name and Address
       (Block Letters)

Address ............................................................

.....................................................

Date of Birth.............../................./.................

| | V. | Sph. | Cyl. | Axis | Prism | Base | V.A. | ADD | Near V.A. | Previous corrected visual acuity |
|---|---|---|---|---|---|---|---|---|---|---|
| R.E. | | | | | | | | | | |
| L.E. | | | | | | | | | | |

To Dr. ...........................................................................................    Date ..............................

...................................................................

I am referring this patient to you because

                                                      (continue overleaf if necessary)

If you refer the patient to hospital please ........... that ....... ist this form complete.

If you do not refer the patient please ........................ w a ....... eturn it to me.

Date .................................... .......................................................

**SECTION 2.** For Gene ....... ic ....... th

   1. Patient seen and .......... 3 ........... M.P./O.O. on ......................................

Or   2. To the Consultant ............ yst ...........................................Hospital

   I should be obliged if .... would see the patient named above in view of the findings recorded and the following history

                                               (continue overleaf if necessary)

| FOR HOSPITAL USE | Date | |
|---|---|---|
| Section 3 sent to O.M.P./O.O. | ........................ | Signed........ ............................................. |
| G.M.P. advised | ........................ | Date................................................................ |

**SECTION 3.** Reply by the General Medical Practitioner (if the patient is not referred to hospital) or Ophthalmologist

To .................................................................................................O.M.P./O.O.

Mr./Mrs./Miss ...................... .......................... ......................................................of

............ ..................................................................... may ........ be supplied
                                                         should not

with glasses under the General Ophthalmic Services.

Remarks:

                                               (continue overleaf if necessary)

Name and Address of General Medical Practitioner    Signed..............................................
   or Hospital

                                         Date.................................................

                                             G.O.S. 18

# Example contract of employment

STATEMENT OF PARTICULARS AND TERMS OF EMPLOYMENT

Pursuant to Section 1, Employment Protection (Consolidation) Act 1978

To: Name of Employee: ........................................................................

Address: ..................................................................................................

From: Smith & Jones, Optometrists, 524 High Street, Anytown

Your employment began on: ........................................ 19 ........

(No employment with a previous employer counts as part of your period of continuous employment with us.)

1. You are employed as ...............................................................

2. Your remuneration will be £ .............. per ........................ payable ........................

3. Your normal hours of work are:

    Mondays to Fridays from .......... am to ........... pm
    and        from .......... pm to ........... pm

   Every day shown as a working day will be regarded as a 'qualifying day' for statutory sick pay.

4. Holidays and holiday pay

   a)  The holiday year runs from 1st January to 31st December.

   b)  You will be expected to take not more than ........ working days' holiday at one time, although this arrangement may be varied with the prior approval of the Firm. Normally, .......... working days holiday will be taken during the summer months and the remaining holiday during the rest of the year.

   c)  The dates of all holiday leave must be agreed with the Management.

   d)  Holiday entitlement must normally be taken within the relevant calendar year, but with the consent of the Firm may be carried over until the 31st March of the ensuing year. No payment will be made in lieu of holiday entitlement not taken unless the circumstances are exceptional or on termination of employment.

   e)  For new staff members, paid holidays may be granted in advance of it actually being earned but if the employment is terminated by either party before the end of the holiday year, payment for any excess holiday granted in excess of entitlement will be deducted from your salary.

*f*)　Calculation of holiday entitlement:
  i)　Year of joining: ................. days' holiday with pay for every complete calendar month of continuous service up to the end of the calendar year.
  ii)　Each complete holiday year thereafter: ............... days' holiday with pay.
  iii)　On termination of employment: .................days' holiday with pay for each completed calendar month of continuous working service in the current holiday year.

From this will be taken the holiday already received and a pro rata salary adjustment made for any difference.

*g*)　Statutory holidays. New Year's Day, Good Friday, Easter Monday, May Day, Spring Bank Holiday, Summer Bank Holiday, Christmas Day, Boxing Day and holidays declared by the Queen shall be recognised and observed as statutory holidays. When any statutory holiday falls on a non-working day, another day's holiday will be given.

5.　Sickness or injury

*a*)　If you are unable to work due to sickness or injury, notify the Firm by telephone on your first day's absence from work. Evidence of incapacity in the form of a sickness benefit claim form (SCT1) or similar statement of illness will be required in respect of an absence lasting less than seven days and must be sent to the Firm on or before the third day of absence. A National Insurance medical certificate or other medical certificate will be required for any absence lasting eight days or more. An interview on your return to work may be necessary.

*b*)　After taking into account any statutory sick pay or state benefits receivable, you are eligible to receive during any period of certified absence from work due to sickness or incapacity:
  i)　full pay as set out in section 2 for the first ...................................
  ii)　....................pay for the next ...................................

*c*)　On the fourth day of absence you will be entitled to statutory sick pay. You will not have to wait the three days if a period of sickness absence is 'linked' with a previous period of absence, that is if you are absent for a second period of four or more consecutive days within two weeks of a previous absence.

*d*)　Sick pay in excess of the above contractual arrangements may be given at the discretion of the Firm.

*e*)　There is no entitlement to contractual sick pay during any period where maternity leave may be claimed.

6.　Absence other than for certified personal sickness

*a*)　Paid or unpaid leave of absence may be granted in the case of a bereavement or sickness of a dependant at the discretion of the Firm.

*b*)　Attending at court on jury service or as a witness. Special leave will be granted if you are required to attend court on witness or jury service. This will amount to pay for the hours spent on service within the hours of a normal working day less such allowances as are paid by the Court.

7.　Pension

The Firm does not operate a contributory pension scheme and you are contracted into the state scheme.

8.　Notice required on termination of employment

*a*)　You must give the Firm a minimum of four weeks' notice of termination of employment, although a longer period of notice would be appreciated.

*b*)　The Firm will give you a minimum of four weeks' notice of termination of employment.

*c*)   The period of notice may be waived by mutual written agreement.

9.   Disciplinary procedure

*a*)   If your performance does not reach the standard required by the Principal, or you commit a minor act of misconduct, then the Principal may issue a formal verbal warning. This warning may be entered on your personnel file and it will be made clear that this is the first stage of the disciplinary procedure.

*b*)   A written warning will be given if, after one or more verbal warnings, your standard of conduct or performance does not improve, or as a first stage of the procedure if your poor performance or conduct is more serious.  A disciplinary interview will be held between you and the Principal, when it will be made clear that dismissal could result if there is no improvement in conduct or performance within a specified time.

10. Dismissal

This will take place if:

*a*)   The required improvement requested in the written warning has not occurred, *or*

*b*)   Further misconduct occurs after a written warning has been given, *or*

*c*)   Gross misconduct occurs which will normally result in instant dismissal.

You may be asked not to work the notice period but will receive payment in lieu.

11. Grievance procedure

If you have a complaint regarding your employment you should first raise the matter with the Principal.
If the matter remains unresolved it should be submitted in writing to the Principal who, after any necessary consultations, will give his decision in writing.
If the matter still remains unresolved and it concerns the statutory sick pay scheme, then you may raise the matter with the Insurance Officer using the National Insurance Appeals Procedure.  If it concerns a disciplinary matter involving dismissal, then you may refer the matter to the Advisory, Conciliation and Arbitration Service (ACAS).

12. Representation

You have the right to be represented or accompanied by a colleague of your choice at any of the procedures outlined in 9, 10 or 11 above.

13. Statement of Terms of Employment

Issued ......................................................... 19 .......

Signed ..............................................................................
(by or on behalf of the Employer)

# Optical bodies and associations

### Association of Dispensing Opticians

The ADO represents qualified dispensing opticians. The address is:
22 Nottingham Place
London W1M 4AT

### Association of Optical Practitioners

The AOP represents the political interests of the ophthalmic optician/
optometrist. Approximately half of all qualified ophthalmic opticians/
optometrists are members. The address is:
Bridge House
233–234 Blackfriars Road
London SE1 8NW

### British College of Ophthalmic Opticians (Optometrists)

Representing over 90 per cent of qualified ophthalmic opticians/
optometrists, the BCOO maintains professional standards, organises
professional examinations and monitors the academic standards of the
profession. The address is:
10 Knaresborough Place
London SW5 0TG

### British Contact Lens Association

Ophthalmic opticians/optometrists and dispensing opticians with a special
interest in contact lenses may join this association. The address is:
51 Strathyre Avenue
London SW16 4RA

## Federation of Independent British Optometrists

Ophthalmic opticians/optometrists who support the idea of an independent profession giving primary health care service make up this organisation. The address is:

12 St Mary's Road
Market Harborough
Leicestershire LE16 7DU

## General Optical Council

Established under the terms of the Opticians Act 1958, the GOC has a duty to protect the public interest by setting required standards for the ophthalmic optical/optometric profession. The address is:

41 Harley Street
London W1N 2DJ

## International Optometric and Optical League

An organisation open to associations world wide which represents ophthalmic opticians/optometrists. The aim is to promote standards of optometric eye care and improve optometric training in developing countries. The address is:

10 Knaresborough Place
London SW5 0TG

## Optical Information Council

Subsidised by voluntary contribution from industry and ophthalmic opticians/optometrists and from dispensing opticians, this organisation has attempted to advertise the need for good eye care and acts as a public information service. The address is:

Temple Chambers
Temple Avenue
London EC4Y 0DT

## Worshipful Company of Spectacle Makers

The oldest established of the remaining professional organisations, this Company now has forsaken its examining role in ophthalmic optics/ optometry, and has become more involved in the manufacturing industry. The address is:

Apothecaries Hall
Blackfriars Lane
London EC4V 6EL

# Index